STEPPING STONES TO NATURE

by

ROBERT O. BALE

Boys' Program Director
Elmira Neighborhood House
Elmira, New York

BURGESS PUBLISHING COMPANY
426 South 6th Street — Minneapolis 15, Minnesota

Burgess
CAMPING SERIES
Consulting Editors
BARBARA ELLEN JOY and MARJORIE CAMP

CREATIVE NATURE CRAFTS . . . . Bale
STEPPING STONES TO NATURE . . . . Bale
INSPIRATIONAL POETRY FOR CAMP
   AND YOUTH GROUPS . . . . Berger
DANCE A WHILE . . . . Harris, Pittman, Waller
WORKBOOK FOR CAMP
   COUNSELOR TRAINING . . . . Hartwig
TEACHING OF TENNIS . . . . Jaeger, Leighton
CAMP CRAFT . . . . Joy
CAMPING . . . . Joy
THE NATURE PROGRAM AT CAMP . . . . Nickelsburg
A MANUAL OF RIDING . . . . Orr
GAMES for the ELEM. SCHOOL GRADES . Richardson
GAMES for JR. and SR. HIGH SCHOOLS . Richardson
BEGINNING SYNCHRONIZED SWIMMING . . Spears
TALKS FOR TEENAGERS . . . . Welch

Copyright © 1960
by
Robert O. Bale

Library of Congress Catalog Card No. 60-8275

Printed in the United States of America

PREFACE

This book is intended as an aid to instructors, camp leaders, teachers, and other youth group leaders who have need for individual and group activities and projects that help to develop an interest in nature.

"Stepping Stones to Nature" describes the book well, for each activity and project is another stepping stone towards an aroused interest in the weather, the sun, the stars, growing things, earth, air, and water.

Nature is so common; so all-around us; that we often do not see nor appreciate its beauties. There is much that we never see; and much more that must be carefully examined or called to our attention, to be seen and appreciated.

Boys and girls, and most adults too, need to be shown the beauties of nature; to have the beauty in a leaf, a stone, a shell, a cloud, in the stars, even in a snake or spider, pointed out to them.

Learning to see and appreciate the beautiful things in nature gives a satisfaction that cannot be gained from material things; a nearness to God, the Creator; a nearness that is so much easier to feel when we are close to the things He has created.

This book, like its forerunner, "Creative Nature Crafts", also used handicrafts employing materials found in woods, fields, streams, and lakes, as a means of arousing interest in, and building a love for nature study.

"When we are out of doors, we are mighty close to the Eternal".

TABLE OF CONTENTS

page

Preface i

Foreword ix

Weather Forecasting Equipment You Can Build . . . 1

    Seeing Air Pressure at Work 1
    Let's Make a Barometer. 4
    A Simple Barometer 4
    A Bottle Barometer. 5
    A Mercury Barometer 7
    An Aneroid Barometer 8
    Let's Make a Rain Gauge 9
    Let's Make a Weather Vane 11
    Let's Make a Wind Gauge 12

Find True North By the Stars 15

Tell Time By the Stars 15

Find True North By the Sun 18

Tell Time By the Sun 20

    Let's Make a Sun Dial 20

Make Your Own Planetarium. 25

    A Cardboard Planetarium (Projector). 25
    A Papier-Mache Heaven. 26
    Blue Printing the Stars 26

Fire Without Matches 28

Fire By Friction   28
Fire With Flint and Steel   31

Crafts For Studying Animals and Plants   34

Let's Build an Antarium   34
Traps for Collecting   37
    A Water Insect Trap   37
    A Cricket Trap   37
    A Grasshopper Trap   38
    A Nightcrawler Trap   38
    A Trap for Mealworms   38
    A Trap for Flying Insects   39
    A Trap for Minnows   39
    A Crayfish Trap   40
Live Animal Traps   41
    A Paper Trap   41
    A Tin Can Trap   42
    A Trap-door Trap   43
    A Figure Four Trap   46
    Trapping With a Camera   49
Cages For an Insect Zoo   51
    A Cork-pin Cage for Crickets   51
    A House for Crickets   52
    A Home for Polliwogs   52
    A Caterpillar Cage   53

Growing Things   55

Seeing Seeds Grow   55
Watching Slips and Twigs Take Root   55
How Bulbs Develop Into Plants   56
Some Plants Start From Roots   56
Watching Grass Grow   57

Making a Science Observation Mount   58

The Riker Mount   58

Crafts Using Native Materials   60

Native Clays 60
Indian Paints 64
Juice Paints 67
Make a Starch Paint 68
Natural Dyes 69
Seed Painting 72
Fungus Pictures 72
Basket Making Materials 73
Pine Needle Crafts 75
    A Pine Needle Broom 75
    A Pine Needle Brush 76
A Corn Husk Brush 77
Birch Bark Crafts 78
    Birch Bark Baskets 81
    Birch Bark Novelties 82
Whittling 84
Whittling Projects 86
    Making a Name Tag 87
    Making a Pin 87
    Making a Button 88
    Making an Animal 88
    A Hiking Stick 91
    Making a Noggin 91
    Making a Chess Set 93
Horn Crafts 94
    Make a Bugle 95
    Make a Powder Horn 96
    Make a Horn Cup 97
    Make a Horn Spoon 99
Feather Crafts 100
    Writing Pens or Quills 100
Musical Instruments 101
    Morache 101
    A Gourd Dance Rattle 102
    A Horn Dance Rattle 104
    A Turtle Shell Dance Rattle 105
    A Corn-stalk Violin 107
    A Flute From a Pumpkin Leaf 108
    A Voice Disguiser 108

Bone Crafts 109
    A Neckerchief Slide 109
    Napkin Rings, Finger Rings, Trophies . . . 110
Crafts With Nuts 110
    Pecans 111
    Walnuts 113
    Almonds 114
    Hazel Nuts 115
    Other Nut Buttons 116
    Peach Pits 116
Shell Crafts 117
    A Shell Bracelet 118
    Shell Earrings 118
    Shell Plaques 118
Seed Crafts 119
    Corn Flowers 119
Leaf Pictures 120
    Mullein Rosettes 120
Milkweed Fluff Balls 121
Pomander Balls 121
Balls of Cloves 122
Sachets 122
Magnolia Leaf Skeletons (Angel Feathers) . . . 123
Bayberry Candles 124
Flower Petal Beads 126
Crystallizing Solution for Cards 127
Snowstorm in a Glass Jar 128
Plaster of Paris Book-Ends 129
Using Egg Shells 131
    A Crackle Finish 131
    Egg Decorating 131
Vegetable Block Printing 133
Crayon Batik 134
Two-Color Carnations 134
Leaf Silhouettes 135
Foil Prints of Leaves 135
Shadow Prints of Leaves 135
Waxing Autumn Leaves 136
Preserving Leaves With Glycerine 136

  page

Craft Recipes 137
        High Polish for Wooden Articles 137
        Modeling Dough 137
        Finger Paints 138
        Papier-Mache 138

Selected Bibliography 139

FOREWORD

Youth groups thrive on a program of well planned activity.

Here in "Stepping Stones to Nature" are detailed directions for many activities and projects that fit into the programs of numerous youth groups. Ideas and directions are here for the leader to use with little more preparation on his or her part.

A well planned nature program might include weather forecasting, using equipment built by the boys and girls in the group; a study of the stars, making their own simple planetariums and blueprints of some of the better known constellations; constructing an antarium in which they can observe the well organized life of an ant colony; collecting insects and building cages for an insect zoo; and doing crafts using native materials that are available for the collecting, and then learning to identify those materials used.

The activities and crafts suggested in this book are by no means all of the possibilities. Be sure to check the bibliography at the end of the book for sources of other ideas to add to your nature program.

WEATHER FORECASTING EQUIPMENT YOU CAN BUILD

The weather is probably the most common topic of conservation, and although we can not yet change the weather to suit our plans, we can always change our plans to suit the weather, particularly if we have an idea of what it is going to be like during the next 48 hours or so.

A lot of the weather forecasting that we can do, depends upon our observation of the clouds, wind, sun, etc. Some of this we can do with our senses alone, but some of it requires the assistance of weather forecasting equipment or devices, most of which we can make for ourselves. Let's try out some of them and see how much fun it is, as well as helping us to learn about why we have the weather that we do have.

First let us see what air pressure is, and how it effects things that we can see.

SEEING AIR PRESSURE AT WORK

The weight of the air above us can be measured in tons for there is a pressure of about 15 pounds per square inch exerted on every object on earth. We do not normally feel this weight, but we can see it by a simple experiment.

Obtain a small wooden slat about 2 or 3 inches wide and about 2 feet long and lay it on a table with one end extending about 6 inches over the edge of the table. On top of this slat, lay several thicknesses of newspaper. Push down on the end of the slat slowly. You will see that the newspaper rises where the other end of the slat lifts it up.

- 1 -

Try it again, but this time strike the slat hard at the extreme end which extends off the table. What happened? You probably broke the end off the slat. Did the newspaper rise as it did before? No.

When the slat is hit sharply, the air does not have time to flow under the newspaper, and most of the weight of the air is felt on the top of the newspaper, holding it down. Try to figure how much the weight of the air might be, pushing down on the newspaper. (Multiply the number of square inches of newspaper surface by 15 to get the approximate answer in pounds.)

LET'S SEE AIR PRESSURE WORK IN ANOTHER WAY.

Fill an ordinary drinking glass with water and cover the glass with a small piece of waxed paper. Holding the waxed paper in place with the palm of the hand, turn the glass upside down and carefully remove your hand. The air pressure on the outside will hold the waxed paper in place and the water will remain in the glass.

ANOTHER DEMONSTRATION OF AIR PRESSURE WORKING MIGHT BE THIS ONE:

You will need an empty milk bottle, a piece of rubber balloon, a rubber band, a piece of paper, and a match. Light the piece of paper and drop it into the bottle. Just before it is completely burned, stretch the piece of rubber balloon over the mouth of the bottle and fasten it there with the rubber band.

The burning paper has expanded the paper inside the bottle making some of it escape, and leaving less air inside. As the remaining air cools, the pressure inside the bottle will be less than that on the outside, and the greater pressure of the outside air will make the rubber of the balloon bulge downward inside the neck of the bottle.

A trick may be performed using this
greater outside air pressure. Instead of
the piece of rubber balloon, seal the neck
of the milk bottle with a peeled boiled egg,
just as the paper is finishing burning. As
the air inside the bottle cools, the air pressure on the outside will force the boiled
egg into the bottle.

AIR PRESSURE CAN CRUSH A TIN CAN CAN, TOO.

Take a small tin can with a screw top, such as a syrup can.
Place a small amount of water in the can; set the can on the
stove and bring the water to a boil. As soon as the water
reaches the boiling point, remove the can from the heat and
immediately screw the top on tightly, being careful not to
be burned by the steam. Now run cold water over the can.
Most of the air has been exhausted from the can by replac-
ing it with steam. The steam condenses as the can is
cooled and exerts less pressure allowing the greater air
pressure on the outside to crush the can.

STILL ANOTHER DEMONSTRATION OF AIR PRESSURE CAN BE DONE IN THIS MANNER:

Bore a 1/4" hole through a block of wood, or use a large
spool. Over one end of the hole, place a small piece of
cardboard a little larger than the end of the wooden block
or spool. Stick an ordinary pin through the center of the
cardboard and into the hole, about 1/2
the length of the pin.

Blow through the other end of the hole,
holding the cardboard in place until
beginning to blow, and then releasing
it. The blown air will pass around the
card, creating a low pressure area,
and the greater pressure of the atmospheric air will hold
the cardboard against the end of the wooden block.

LET'S MAKE A BAROMETER

We may not think of the air having weight but it does. Although it is very light, it extends so far above us that there is an average weight of 14.7 lbs. (almost 15 lbs.) of air resting on each square inch of the earth's surface. The air not only rests on our heads, but it also presses in from all sides like a very gentle vise. This would be very uncomfortable if we did not also have just about the same amount of pressure in our lungs pressing outwards.

The weight of the air varies with altitude for higher places will have less air resting on top of them, and consequently less weight or air pressure. The weight of the air is constantly changing from hour to hour and from day to day. Warm air is lighter, and cold air heavier.

The weight of the air, or air pressure, can be measured and used in weather forecasting by an instrument called a barometer which uses the air pressure, as we have seen it demonstrated, in such a manner that it can be measured on a scale or dial.

Changes in air pressure are connected with changes in the weather, consequently changes in air pressure are important in weather forecasting. The greatest air pressure comes just before fair weather, and the lowering of the air pressure is an indication of bad weather coming.

A SIMPLE BAROMETER

MATERIALS NEEDED:

Pint jar

Soft drink bottle

Bluing

Glue or Cement

Small ruler or strip of paper

HOW TO MAKE:

Fill the pint jar almost full of
water to which bluing has
been added.

Fill the soft drink bottle about
2/3 full and turn it upside
down inside the pint jar.

Cement a strip of paper or a
small ruler to the outside
of the soft drink bottle,
marking the level of the
water with a crayon or
pencil.

Notice the changes in the level of the water from day to day.
When the level rises here, we say that the barometer
is rising and we may look for good weather. When the
level drops, it indicates a change in the weather.

A BOTTLE BAROMETER

This type of barometer shows more accuracy than the simple barometer just described.

MATERIALS NEEDED:

Large beverage bottle

1/4" diameter glass tubing approximately the same height
as the bottle.

Tight fitting cork for bottle, preferably a rubber cork with
hole in center the same diameter as the glass tube.

Strip of adhesive tape about 4 inches long

Water

HOW TO MAKE:

Fill the bottle about 1/5 full of water.

Run the glass tubing through the cork and fit the cork tightly
   into the bottle.   The tube should reach down into the
   water.

Fasten the tape to the side of the bottle, starting about 1"
   below the level of the water and extending about 3"
   above the top of the water level.   Mark the tape in
   inches, quarter inches and eighth inches.   If you have
   access to a reliable barometer, read the air pressure
   on it and write this pressure on the tape at the mark
   nearest the level of the water in the bottle.   Use this
   as a future reference mark.

HOW TO USE:

Set the bottle in a vertical position.
As fair weather approaches, and
the air pressure increases, the
weight of the air will press down
harder on the column of water in
the open end of the glass tube.   This
will force the water up higher inside
the bottle.   Watch this water level
(in the bottle, not the tube).   As
long as it is high, or continues to
rise, we can say that the barometer
is rising and we can look for fair
weather.   When bad weather is ap-
proaching the barometer will drop
and the level of the water in the bottle will go down while the level of
the water will rise in the glass tube
because of the lower air pressure
on top of this water.   (Do not con-
fuse this barometer with the mercury barometer next described.   In
the Bottle Barometer just described,

we read the level of the water in the bottle, not in the glass tube. In the mercury barometer, we read the level of the mercury in the glass tube.)

You may find that it will be necessary to add a little water occasionally because of evaporation, but never add more than enough to replace that which was lost.

A MERCURY BAROMETER

A more accurate barometer may be made as described in the following paragraphs.

MATERIALS NEEDED:

A piece of glass tubing 36" long and 1/4"
    in diameter

A small dish

Mercury (about 1/4 cup)

A small 3-cornered file

Pieces of wood 40" X 3", and 6" X 6"

HOW TO MAKE:

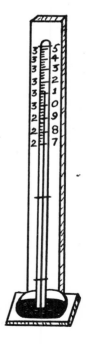

One end of the glass tube is sealed by melting it in a gas flame. When the glass has cooled, a scale of inches is marked on the glass tube using the 3-cornered file to scratch the markings onto the glass. Start the markings 1" from the sealed end of the tube, and progressing towards the open end. The first marking will be 35 inches, the next 34 inches, etc. These figures may be written on the wooden mount holding the glass tube in place. Divide the inch markings into half, quarter, and eighth inches.

Fill the tube with mercury, place the finger over the open
end, and carefully invert it into the small dish filled
about half full with mercury. Be careful that none of
the mercury spills from the glass tube before the open
end is beneath the surface of the mercury in the dish.
Fasten to a wooden frame.

HOW TO USE:

In fair weather, the mercury will stand around 30" or higher
in the tube and in bad weather it will usually fall below 30".
The important thing however, is not whether the barometer
is high or low, but whether it is rising or falling. A rising
barometer normally indicates the approach of good weather
and a falling barometer, the approach of bad weather. A
sudden drop of 2" or more might indicate a very severe
storm on its way.

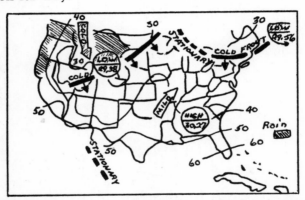

A weather map shows air pressure, temperature, precipitation, and general wind
directions.
The forecast with this copy of a weather map was as follows:
"Precipitation will be confined to showers in Montana, northern Idaho,
Washington, coastal Oregon and northern California. It will continue
cool in the Atlantic States and become somewhat cooler in the nor-
thern Plains and northern Rockies. It will be warmer in the Mississippi,
Ohio, and Tennessee valleys and the South and central Plains."

AN ANEROID BAROMETER

An aneroid barometer is another type of barometer which
shows changes in the air pressure with equipment similar
to our demonstration of air pressure using the rubber balloon and the jar with the burning paper inside.

MATERIALS NEEDED:

A quart jar

A rubber balloon

A drinking straw

Rubber cement

Ruler

Rubber band

HOW TO MAKE:

Stretch a piece of the rubber balloon over the neck of the
quart jar and fasten it tightly with the rubber band.

To the center of the rubber diaphragm over the top of the
jar, fasten one end of the drinking straw with rubber
cement.

Fasten the ruler perpendicular to the ground on any convenient surface, and set the quart jar so that the drinking
straw almost touches the ruler. Once or twice each
day, read the height of the end of the straw on the ruler.
Differences in height indicates changes in the air pressure. When the air pressure is higher, the end of the
straw will indicate a higher reading on the ruler.

Be sure that the quart jar is away from heat, either artifi-
cial or the heat of the sun, for such direct heat will
change the air pressure on the inside of the jar, making
your observations inaccurate.

LET'S MAKE A RAIN GAUGE

A rain gauge may be made from any convenient straight
sided container, though a glass container is easiest to read.

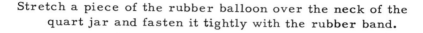

Be certain that the bottom of the container is level, and that the sides do
not slant.   Otherwise the measure-
ments will not be accurate.

MATERIALS NEEDED:

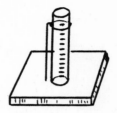

A verticle sided glass container such
as a test-tube, jar, or glass.

A 3-cornered file

A metal or wooden standard to hold the gauge upright.

HOW TO MAKE:

Mark the glass in 1/8", 1/4", 1/2", and inch divisions
starting at the bottom. . Use the file to make scratch
marks on the glass.

Make a standard to hold the gauge upright.   This may be
simply a hole bored in a wooden block, or it may be a
wire frame bent to shape to hold the gauge upright.

HOW TO USE:

The rain gauge should be placed in the open where it is not
sheltered by trees or buildings.   Read the amount of
rainfall directly from your marks on the gauge.   Always be sure to empty the gauge after any rainfall so
that the next precipitation may be measured accurately.
Take your readings as soon as possible after the rain
ends and before any evaporation takes place.

Keep records of the rainfall in your area.

(Glass rain gauges are not to be used during freezing
weather for freezing water will cause the glass to
break.)

To measure small amounts of rainfall easily, we can make
another simple measuring device.

Obtain a second verticle-sided container with a smaller diameter than the one used for the rain gauge. Calibrate
this with the rain gauge in the following manner:

Pour 1/8" of water into the rain gauge, then pour this
from the gauge into the smaller container. With the
file, mark the level of this water and label it 1/8". Do
the same for each of the other marks on the rain gauge.
This will make small amounts of precipitation easier to
read, for when the rain water is poured from the gauge
into the smaller container, slight amounts, or differences will be more pronounced on the marking scale.

LET'S MAKE A WEATHER VANE

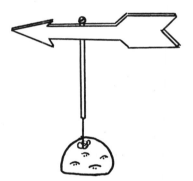

There are two important
things to remember in making
a weather vane. It must turn
freely, and there must be a
large surface at the back of
the vane to catch the wind and
made the front end point into
the direction from which the
wind is coming.

MATERIALS NEEDED:

Cardboard 4" X 10"

Plastic straw

Small screw to fit in end of straw

Household cement

Straight piece of heavy wire, or section of wire coat hanger
8" - 10" long

Potato, plasticene, or piece of wood for the base of the
weather vane

HOW TO MAKE:

Fold the cardboard into half, lengthways, and cut into arrow
shape, leaving the fold uncut at the top along the tail of
the arrow.

Find the balance point of the arrow and insert the plastic
straw through the arrow at this point, between the two
sections of cardboard.

Cement the cardboard arrow together and the plastic straw
in place.

Cement the small screw into the upper end of the plastic
straw.

Slip the straw over the wire and insert the other end of the
wire in a potato with the bottom sliced off so that it
will stand. (Wood, plasticene, or other support may
be used.)

When this weather vane is taken out of doors, it will quickly react to the wind with the arrow pointing to the direction from which the wind is coming. Use a compass
to determine the direction of the wind, making sure the
reading of the compass is parallel to the arrow of the
weather vane and the compass needle is on the N
(north) of the compass.

LET'S MAKE A WIND GAUGE

A wind gauge, or anemometer, is an instrument used to
measure the velocity or speed of the wind. It is made using
a number of cups to catch the wind and cause the instrument
to spin on its axis. A count of the number of revolutions
per minute is used to determine the speed or velocity.

MATERIALS NEEDED:

2 strips of heavy cardboard
    2" X 8"

4 medium sized paper cups

1 plastic drinking straw

Small screw to fit in end of
    straw

Household cement

Stiff wire or coat hanger wire, 8" - 10" long

Potato, wooden block, or plasticene for base

HOW TO MAKE:

Fold the two strips of cardboard in half, lengthways, making two folded strips one inch wide.

Cut slits in the paper cups, 1" from the tops of the cups,
and 1" wide on opposite sides of each cup.

Insert the plastic drinking straw through holes in the center
edges of each cardboard strip. Cement in place with
the cardboard strips at right angles to each other. The
top of the straw should extend 1" above the tops of the
cardboard strips. Cement the screw into the end of the
straw.

Slip the ends of the cardboard strips through the slits in the
four paper cups, one cup on each end of the strips.
Slide them to an equal distance (about 1/2") from the
ends of the strips and cement them in place. The cups
on the opposite ends of each strip, should face in opposite directions so that as the gauge revolves, each
cup will catch the wind.

Slice the potato to make it stand, and push the wire into the potato in a vertical position. Place the open end of the plastic straw over the wire. The gauge should turn freely when you blow into one of the paper cups.

Color one of the paper cups in a contrasting color so that the revolutions may be counted easily.

Set the gauge or anemometer outside. Count the number of turns per minute. Check the daily paper for the approximate wind velocity for that day, and then use the number of turns per minute to calibrate your own wind gauge or anemometer.

If the wind was reported at 15 miles per hour, and you counted 80 turns per minute, you would know that 80 turns indicated 15 miles per hour. Thusly 40 turns per minute would indicate 7-1/2 miles per hour, while 60 turns per minute would be about 12 miles per hour, etc.

FIND TRUE NORTH BY THE STARS

Probably the easiest of the constellations to recognize is the
"Big Dipper", also known as Ursa Major, or the Great Bear.
It is shaped like a dipper and is always located in the north,
revolving around Polaris, the North or Pole Star.

The two stars at the end of the dipper are known as the
"pointers". Locate these and draw an imaginary line
through them. This line will extend to the North Star. The
point on the horizon directly beneath this star, is true north.

TELL TIME BY THE STARS

Before the advent of the modern clock and watch, the art of
telling time by both the sun and stars, was an important
part of a person's education. Now it has fallen into disuse
and few persons know how to tell time at night without a
watch.

We do have a star clock in the heavens, however, and it is
one that is amazingly accurate if we but learn how to use it.
With a little practice to develop skill, a person can estimate

the local standard time at night with an accuracy that will amaze those who do not know how it is done. An error of not more than 15 minutes is easily possible when you learn how to read the dial of the star clock.

Our star clock is composed of the North Star and the Big. Dipper, or rather the two pointers of the Big Dipper.

We must remember that the Big Dipper goes completely around the North Star once every 24 hours.

HOW TO READ THE STAR CLOCK:

Stand facing the North Star and imagine that it is exactly in the center of a large clock dial with the numeral 12 directly above the North Star. The hand of the clock is a straight line leading from the two pointers of the Big Dipper to the North Star.

Now follow these three steps:

1- Read the apparent time on the star clock to the nearest quarter hour. The point where the hand crosses the imaginary clock dial will give you this apparent time.

2- To this number, add the number of months that have elapsed since the beginning of the year.

3- Take the number that you have as a result of the above, and double it. Subtract your answer from 28-1/4. If your answer was larger than 28-1/4, subtract it from 52-1/4.

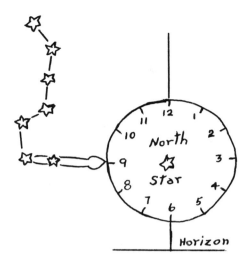

The final answer that you get, following the above directions, should be the local time, correct within a few
minutes, and reckoned since the previous midnight.
(If your final answer is more than 12, it would mean
sometime in the P. M. , for the first 12 hours would
be A. M.. For instance, an answer of 23-1/2 would
make the local time 11:30 P. M.)

The accuracy of your final answer depends upon the accuracy with which you read the imaginary dial of the star
clock. Practice for a while and see just how good you can
get.

Read the above star clock dial and figure the time with us.
The date is June 15.
The approximate time on the star clock dial is 9:00 or
simply 9
Add the number of months since Jan. 1   5-1/2
14-1/2
Double the result - 2 X 14-1/2 equals 29
Since 29 is more than 28-1/4 we substract it from
52-1/4. This equals 23-1/4.
23-1/4 hours since the previous midnight gives us a
local standard time of 11:15 P. M.

FIND TRUE NORTH BY THE SUN

When the sun shines and we know the time of day, we can get a close estimate of where true north lies, but if we want to know exactly where true north lies, we can find it in the following manner. This project will take the most of one sunny day to complete.

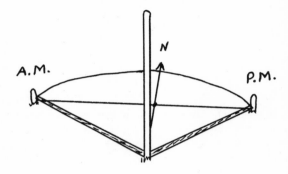

HOW TO DO IT:

In the early morning of a sunny day, drive a stick of about four feet in length into the ground in any convenient flat area where the shadow of the stick may easily be observed.

Drive a peg into the ground at the end of the shadow of the stick. Using the distance from the foot of the upright stick to the peg as a radius, draw an arc with the base of the upright stick as the center. This is easily done by tying a cord around the base of the stick and tying a small stick to the cord where the cord touches the peg, then drawing a circle on the ground using the stick tied in the cord as a marker.

As the sun rises in the sky, the shadow of the upright stick will become shorter and shorter, but as the sun starts to go down in the afternoon, the shadow will start to grow longer. When the shadow once again touches the outline of the circle drawn on the ground, in the late afternoon, mark this spot with another peg.

Now draw a straight line between the two pegs in the ground, and mark the point one half the distance between the two pegs. A line drawn from the base of the upright stick, and through this halfway point, will be pointing to true north.

TELL TIME BY THE SUN

We have just learned how to tell time by the stars. During the daytime we can use the sun to tell us the time. The most accurate method is by making and using a sun dial which is actually nothing more than an upright stick casting its shadow. We can use the shadow of the stick to read the time just as we do the hour hand of the clock.

LET'S MAKE A SUN DIAL

HOW A SUN DIAL WORKS -

When the earth spins on its axis, it appears that the sun is making a big circle in the sky around the axis of the earth. We make use of this in reading the time by the sun.

By pointing a stick in the same direction as the earth's axis, so that it casts its shadow on a flat surface parallel to the equator, we have a shadow that will keep accurate time with the passage of the sun across the sky.

MATERIALS NEEDED:

A good Atlas or map showing the latitude where you are (See attached map)

2 pieces of wood 10" X 15" X 3/4"	Carpenters' level
2 pieces of wood 4" X 8" X 3/4"	1/4" drill
Ruler	Glue or cement
Pencil	Compass for drawing circle
Handsaw	Protractor
Finishing nails 1-1/2" long	Magnetic compass for finding east-west line
Dowel 4" X 1/4"	

HOW TO MAKE:

Look up your latitude on the preceding map or in your Atlas.
Subtract the latitude from 90 degrees. The answer
that you get is used as follows: Cut the two 4" X 8"
pieces of wood into wedge-shaped pieces (like a piece
of pie) with the angle at the point of the wedge being the
same as the number of degrees in your answer above.
Use the protractor to measure this angle on the wood
before sawing it out.

(Example - New York City is at a latitude of 41 degrees.
90 degrees minus 41 degrees equals 49 degrees. We
use 49 degrees for the angle of the point of the wedge
for a sun dial to be used in the New York City area.)

Take one of the 10" X 15" pieces of wood and draw a base
line parallel to one of its long sides and 1" from the
edge. Measure to the center of this line (7-1/2 inches
from each end), and at this point place the point of the
compass, marking a semi-circle on the board with a
radius of 6".

Lay your protractor along the
base line with the center
of the protractor at the
center of the line, and
mark off 12 angles of 15
degrees each. Draw lines
from the center of the
base line, through each of
these 15 degree points to
touch the line of the semi-
circle which you drew.

Lay the board on the table
with the semi-circle a-
way from you and the
base line nearest you,
and label the lines you
have just drawn, starting

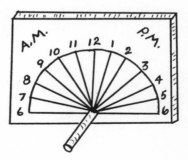

on the left with 6:00 A. M. , then 7:00 A. M. , etc. , progressing towards the right, and ending with 6:00 P. M. at the far right.

Drill a 1/4" hole at the center of the base line and glue the dowel in the hole. The dowel must be vertical to the board.

Now fasten the two boards to the wedge-shaped pieces of wood with the boards touching along the edge nearest the 12 o'clock marking on your sun dial, and the point of the wedge where the boards meet. (See illustration).

Your sun dial is complete, but before using, it must be placed in the correct position.

Positioning the sun dial -

The bottom of the dial must be level, and the edge where the two boards meet must run east and west.

Use the carpenter's level to set the bottom board of the dial in a level position.

Now use the magnetic compass, turning or rotating the dial until the line where the boards are joined runs in a true east-west line.

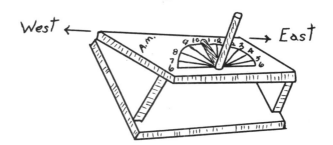

Reading the sun dial -

If you have done each of the steps correctly, the dowel is
    now parallel to the earth's axis, and the top board will
    be parallel to the plane of the equator.

The shadow of the dial can now be used to read the time di-
    rectly from the sun dial.

What time is it in New York City on the sun dial illustrated?

MAKE YOUR OWN PLANETARIUM

Children as well as adults are intrigued and mystified by the stars shining so brightly so many millions of miles above them. In ancient days the stars had the same mystery and stories or legends were told to show from whence came the stars.

These legends are the origins of many of the names of the constellations that we see in the night sky; the identical constellations that were seen hundreds of years ago.

There is plenty of help available in books and charts for beginners, but sometimes it is easier, and more fun in the bargain, if we make our own small planetariums and learn what we are to look for before we look at the whole sky at once and become confused by the multitude of stars.

A CARDBOARD PLANETARIUM – (PROJECTOR)

Using any small cardboard carton, preferably a round cardboard box, select any of the well known constellations and, from a star chart, locate the major stars of this constellation on one end of the cardboard carton. A suggestion is to start with perhaps the easiest one, the Big Dipper (Ursa Major) and include the North Star. (See illustration)

Using a sharp tool, make a hole in the box where you have located each star of the constellation.

To use - place a light bulb inside the carton, or use a bright flashlight, shining light from the inside of the carton through the holes, and projecting the constellation on the ceiling of the room. Of course the room must be dark.

As a boy or girl learns the constellations, let them make a
   scrapbook showing the stars, using gummed silver
   stars on a deep blue construction paper background.

Use several cartons and make a number of the better known
   constellations.   Learn the legend of the constellations
   too.   Good books about the stars are listed in the bibliography at the end of this book.

A PAPIER—MACHE HEAVEN

A map of the night sky can be made from papier-mache.

HOW TO MAKE:

Blow up a round balloon.   Tie the mouth of the balloon to
   hold air.   Using a paste and strips of newspaper, cover
   one half of the balloon with paste and then with strips of
   paper, building up to about 8 layers of paste and paper,
   then allowing the papier-mache to dry thoroughly.

When it is well dried, remove the balloon and trim the paper
   into hemispherical shape.   Paint this hemisphere with
   dark blue airplane dope or tempera paint.

Using any good star map, locate the positions of the major
   constellations for either the summer or the winter sky,
   marking the four horizons, north, south, east, and
   west.

With a sharp pointed tool, punch holes for the stars you have
   located.

Hang your papier-mache heavens from the ceiling, placing
   a light inside to make the stars shine.

BLUE PRINTING THE STARS

Obtain a box of small gummed stars from a stationery store.
Arrange the stars on a piece of glass according to the var-

ious constellations, and then use these for making either blue prints or ozalid prints.

On each print, leave a part of the paper to print white, and write in the legend of that constellation. Use these in a star scrapbook.

FIRE WITHOUT MATCHES

FIRE BY FRICTION

Did you ever try to rub two sticks together to start a fire, and then give up wondering how it could have ever been done successfully? I have, too, but that was before I had instructions on how to do it correctly.

It is easy to start a fire by friction if you know how, but rather hopeless when you do not. With some experience you can get your first sparks in less than 10 seconds, and have a good fire burning within one minute. Try lighting your next campfire this way, but get your materials ready and practice first to make sure that you have the knack of doing it correctly.

The surest and easiest method is with a bow-drill.

The wood used should be soft enough to wear away, but also hard enough so that plenty of heat is produced in the process; and it should burn easily.

The best woods are these: Balsam fir, red cedar, white cedar, larch, basswood, white pine, cypress, cottonwood, poplar, sycamore, yucca, willow, and soft maple.

To make sure that your wood is good for fire making, use this simple test: If the dust that runs out of the notch in your fire-board is coarse and brown, the wood is too soft; and if it is very fine and there is not much of it, the wood is too hard.

MATERIALS NEEDED:

A bow - a slightly curved stick of almost any kind of wood, about 27" long, and 1/2" to 5/8" thick. Ash is very good.

A leather or rawhide thong, long enough to be tied at each end of the bow.

A drill socket - preferably a pine or hemlock knot about 4-1/2" long and 2" wide, shaped to fit the hand.

A drill - made of well dried wood of one of the varieties listed above; about 12" long, and 1/2" to 3/4" thick.

The fire-board - 1/2" to 3/4" thick and of any convenient length and width for carrying easily. It should be of the same kind of wood as the drill.

Tinder.

Fire-pan - a small chip for catching the wood dust and the glowing coal.

HOW TO MAKE:

The Bow - Cut shallow notches about one inch from each end of the bow, or drill a 3/16" hole one inch from one end.

Tie the thong around the notches, or thread through the hole and tie, merely wrapping the thong around the other end of the bow, so that it can be easily tightened. The thong should be loose enough so that it will wrap once around the drill with enough tension to bend the bow a little and to prevent slipping when the drill is twirled.

The Socket - In one side of the pine or hemlock knot or piece of hardwood, cut a shallow pit or socket about 1/4" deep and perhaps 3/8" in diameter. The end of the drill will spin in this socket. (A little grease will help it to spin easier.)

Or cut a larger and deeper pit and cement a small stone in this pit. Cut a small socket or pit in the stone as a place for the drill to spin.

The socket is to be held on the top of the drill while it is being twirled. Pressure on the socket helps to create friction at the other end of the drill.

Trim the knot or socket to fit the hand.

The Drill - Trim the drill to a blunt point at each end, with the end to be placed in the socket being somewhat more pointed than the other end. Whittle the center part of the drill to a six or eight sided shape to help prevent the thong slipping while the drill is being twirled.

The Fire-Board - Cut a series of notches about 2 inches apart along both edges of the board. The notches are 3/4" deep and 1/2" wide at the front. Each notch is for the starting of a separate fire.

Where the notch comes to a point, start a small pit with a knife, drill, or otherwise. This is to hold the end of the fire-drill as drilling is begun.

The Tinder - use any one of the following as it may be available: Finely shredded red cedar bark, white cedar bark, birch bark; inner bark of cottonwood, slippery elm, or chestnut; rope, or even the nest of a field mouse.

To shred, pound between two stones, or scrape with a knife or piece of broken glass.

(Carry a good piece of tinder with you.)

HOW TO USE:

Place the fire-board on the ground with the fire-pan beneath the notch being used. The fire-pan is to catch the wood dust and the spark as it glows.

Pass the leather thong once around the drill so that the drill is on the outside of the thong away from the bow. The thong should be taut and there should be a slight bend in the bow.

Place the bottom end of the drill in the small pit of a notch in the fire-board, and the left foot on the fire-board to hold it in place.

Hold the socket in the
     left hand on the top
     of the drill.

Steady the left arm with
     the left knee so that
     the drill does not
     wobble.

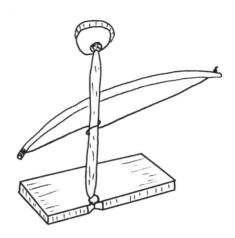

Draw the bow back and
     forth, the full length
     of the bow, and with
     steady, even strokes.
     Keep a constant pres-
     sure on the top of the
     drill, possibly in-
     creasing the pressure
slightly with each stroke. Friction at the notch should
cause the drill to bore into the wood of the fire-board.
The ground-out wood dust will drop from the notch onto
the fire-pan. At first it will be brown, but should quickly turn black and then will start to smoke. As soon as
smoke continues to come from the dust on the fire-pan,
fan it gently until a glowing coal is seen.

Now take a good pinch of tinder, placing it on top of the
     glowing coal, fanning or blowing it gently until it blazes
     up. Add more tinder or very fine kindling and the fire
     is made.

     (Some people prefer to place the tinder on the fire-pan
     beneath the notch in the fire-board, before starting the
     drill. Use the method which seems to work best for
     you.)

FIRE WITH FLINT AND STEEL

Flint and steel have been used to produce sparks and fire
for hundreds of years. Although sparks may be produced
with two pieces of flint alone, the use of a piece of steel
makes it much easier to obtain sparks to start a fire.

MATERIALS NEEDED:

A piece of flint or quartz of a size easily held in the hand or
between the fingers.

A piece of hardened steel such as the back of a jackknife
blade or a piece of an old file.

Charred cotton cloth or cotton rope.

Tinder

HOW TO MAKE:

Charred cotton cloth or cotton rope - Set fire to the cotton
cloth or rope, and when it is burning well, extinguish
it. Select small pieces of the charred cloth or rope to
use. Carry this in a small bottle or plastic bag to keep
it dry and useable.

Tinder - see the directions for making tinder under the
previous section on "Fire by Friction".

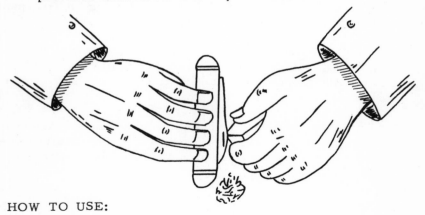

HOW TO USE:

Place a piece of the charred cloth or rope in a small amount
of tinder.

Hold the steel in the right hand, and the flint in the left. With the right hand strike downward with the steel against the edge of the flint so as to send any resulting sparks into the charred cotton. When the cotton starts to smoulder, fan it gently until the tinder bursts into flame. With practice, it is sometimes easier to hold the charred cotton and tinder in the cup in the left hand, and with the flint directly above, making it easier to drive the sparks into the charred cotton.

CRAFTS FOR STUDYING ANIMALS AND PLANTS

LET'S BUILD AN ANTARIUM

Ants are among the most interesting of insects and are easily kept and observed in an antarium or moveable ant colony. This can be one of the most interesting parts of an insect zoo, too.

Here are directions for the construction of an antarium, and for collecting and caring for an ant colony. In your antarium, notice that each of the ants seem to have his own particular job. Some are food collectors; others are carpenters, farmers, garbage collectors, soldiers, nursemaids, road and tunnel builders, etc.

MATERIALS NEEDED:

2 pieces of soft wood 2" X 13-1/2" X 3/4"

2 pieces soft wood 2" X 11" X 3/4"

2 pieces of single thickness window glass 10" X 14"

Small pieces of scrap wire screening

HOW TO MAKE:

Cut a groove lengthways, 1/4" from each edge of each of the four pieces of wood. This groove serves as a slide for the two pieces of glass. The groove should be slightly more than 1/4" deep and wide enough so that the glass slides easily.

Nail the four pieces of wood together as in the illustration, with the 11" pieces as the ends, and the 13-1/2" pieces nailed inside the end pieces, making a frame that is 11" X 15". Fasten with both nails and glue, and be sure to slide the glass into place before attaching the top

piece. Be sure that the grooves are lined up accurately
and that the glass fits squarely.

Bore two 1" holes in the top as illustrated and in the center
cut out a 1" X 2" hole to be used as a door for filling
the antarium and feeding the ant colony.

Cover the two 1" holes with pieces of wire screening tacked
in place. These are for ventilation. Cut a piece of tin
slightly larger than the door. Tack this into place so
that it may be opened when necessary, and closed to
keep the ants from escaping.

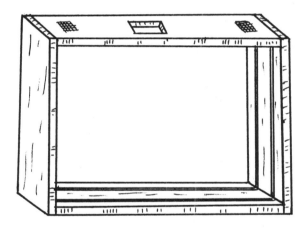

HOW TO USE:

The antarium is intended for the observation of an ant colony.

Collect all of the ants for the antarium from the same colony
or hill, including the queen who is about twice the size
of the other ants, and is usually found deep inside the
ant hill.

Collect enough of the soil from the same ant hill to fill the
antarium about 3/4 full. Place the ants on top of the
soil in the antarium and they will go to work almost

immediately excavating tunnels, hunting for food, laying eggs, caring for the young when they hatch, burying their dead, and all of the other work of an ant colony.

Occasionally place a piece of cotton gauze moistened with water over one of the air holes of the antarium to maintain the proper humidity in the antarium.

Keep the antarium away from direct sunlight, and also away from hot radiators, hot air registers, and other sources of heat.

The ants will need comparatively little food. Add a few tiny pieces of solid food occasionally, and three or four drops of honey or syrup each week. Dampened cake, cookies, icing, and sugar are all good.

To achieve the greatest amount of activity where it can be seen, keep one side of the antarium covered with a dark cloth or a piece of cardboard when you are not observing it.

To make the antarium more interesting, place a tiny amount of watercolor or food coloring with a small brush on certain ants so that you can identify them.

ANOTHER USE FOR THE ANTARIUM:

The antarium makes an excellent device for the observation of seed and plant growth. Fill it about 7/8 full of vermiculite or clean sand. Plant seeds in the antarium and add sufficient water to make the material moist but not wet.

Keep the sides of the glass covered with a dark cloth or cardboard when not under observation. Root growth is of particular interest to observe, under these conditions.

TRAPS FOR COLLECTING

A WATER INSECT TRAP

A small kitchen strainer is most useful for trapping water insects. They need not always be seen to be caught. Draw the strainer through the water beneath the overhanging banks of a stream or pond; lift stones from the bottom and make a quick sweep with the strainer; or simply sweep the strainer through the open water.

Transfer all water insects caught to a jar containing some of the same water from the stream or pond. There they can be studied and identified. Look carefully in the strainer after a sweep through the water, for many of the water insects are so small and transparent that they can scarcely be seen. For this reason a magnifying glass can be very helpful.

A CRICKET TRAP

Obtain a loaf of unsliced bread and slice it in half, either vertically or horizontally. Dig out the center of the loaf.

Cut tunnels through each side of the dug out center to the outsides of the loaf, and then tie the loaf together again with string.

Place the loaf on the ground or on a board and the crickets will soon begin to collect inside the trap. Open the trap occasionally and collect the crickets which have crawled inside.

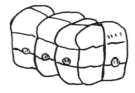

Another type of cricket trap may be made from a wooden box partially filled with moist bran and covered. Cut or bore two or more holes in the sides of box through which the crickets may enter. Place the trap on the ground, and collect the crickets from the inside as you want them.

A GRASSHOPPER TRAP

Grasshoppers are easiest caught
with a net.   Make your own from a
piece of cheesecloth, a heavy wire,
and an old broomstick or dowel for
a handle.

A NIGHTCRAWLER TRAP

Nightcrawlers are large earthworms and may be caught in a
number of ways.   Perhaps the easiest is to go into the garden or on the lawn at night when the ground is moist, during
or after a shower, or a heavy dew.   Use a flashlight, but
take care not to shine it directly on the nightcrawlers for
they are very sensitive to both light and vibration of the soil.
Approach them very carefully, for they can quickly pull back
into the earth.   Grap the exposed end of the worm.   A light
but steady pull will bring the rest of the worm out of the
ground.

Two layers of burlap, laid on the ground where it is moist,
and with moistened bran or poultry mash between the two
layers, will bring the earthworms there to feed and to be
collected.

If earthworms are to be kept for some time for fishing pur-
poses, they must be cared for, too.

Place them in a container with a mixture of half peat or
sphagnum moss, and garden soil.   Sprinkle the surface of
the soil occasionally, but do make it wet.

A little bran or poultry mash sprinkled on the moist soil
will feed the earthworms.   Do not overfeed, however, for
the surplus will soon spoil.

A TRAP FOR MEALWORMS

Mealworms are one of the best baits for such panfish as
perch and sunfish and are easily obtained and raised.

Find a supply of mealworms in some old flour, or in the debris on the floor of your local feed store. (They are sometimes known as Golden Grubs).

Raise the mealworms in a metal container or wooden box covered with screening, for the adults are winged beetles and will fly away if permitted. Keep them in your box to produce more mealworms.

Make several layers of food in the box, separating each layer with a piece of burlap. Each layer should contain 1/4 to 1/2 inch of flour, pieces of raw vegetable such as potatoes, etc., and a few mealworms.

They will soon become adults, which in turn will lay eggs and produce more mealworms. Harvest these when you go fishing. If you need to keep them for any length of time, place them in a small container and store them in a refrigerator where they will be kept cold, but will not freeze.

A TRAP FOR FLYING INSECTS

Some insects fly in the daytime and others at night. A net, the same as that described for catching grasshoppers, may be used for either night or day.

At night, insects are attracted to a bright light. For a variation of insects, set up a light in different locations; near a stream; in an open field; near a house in the city or country; close to a swamp; and in the woods. Watch the multitude of insects attracted to the light, and when a choice variety appears, be ready to net it for your collection.

The principle daytime flying insects to be netted, are the butterflies. Watch for them around flowering shrubs and plants such as lilacs, butterfly weed, etc.

A TRAP FOR MINNOWS

MATERIALS NEEDED:

A large glass jar - 2 qt. to 1 gal. size.

40

Wire screening

Soft wire - about 18"

Tin Shears

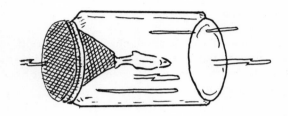

HOW TO MAKE:

Make a funnel or cone shape of the wire screening, of a size
that will slip into the mouth of the glass jar, leaving
enough screening to wrap and tie over the mouth of the
jar. Cut the pointed tip from the wire funnel, leaving
an opening about 1" in diameter.

Place the funnel in the open end of the glass jar; fold the
edges of the funnel over the sides of the jar, and wire
or tie in place. If the wire screening tends to slip from
its funnel shape, sew the funnel with pieces of wire
pulled from the screening.

Bait the trap with a few breadcrumbs and place in the water
where there are minnows.

A CRAYFISH TRAP

Make a trap similar to the minnow trap described above,
but with a larger opening in the wire screen funnel (about
2"), and bait the trap with fish or old raw meat of any kind.

LIVE ANIMAL TRAPS

In Nature Study, we observe living as well as inanimate things. Sometimes this is possible only when we can catch and hold for a while, those small animals that we are otherwise unable to see, except for fleeting glimpses. Among these are the many varieties of mice, moles, chipmunks, squirrels, and others.

The somewhat larger, and occasionally objectionable animals, such as the skunk or coon, are easier photographed than trapped alive and put into the camp zoo or nature center.

Here are listed and described a few of the devices for trapping small wild animals alive and without injury, and for photographing those that we do not wish to trap.

Imprisoned animals need food, shelter, and water, so do not neglect them. Never keep a wild animal in captivity for more than two or three days at the longest, and if possible only long enough to become acquainted with it and learn a few of its habits which may be much different in captivity than in the free state.

A PAPER TRAP

This is probably the simplest trap that can be made.

MATERIALS NEEDED:

Earthenware crock or large
    metal pail

Heavy wrapping paper

String

Bait

HOW TO MAKE:

Cut a sheet of heavy paper, somewhat larger than the top of
the crock or pail, and tie it tightly over the top.

At the center of the paper, cut slits, making a cross of about
5" as illustrated. Place the trap in the woods or fields,
either setting the trap into the ground, or arranging
branches, rocks, or boards for a runway to the top of
the trap.

Use gloves when removing live animals from any trap.

A TIN CAN TRAP

MATERIALS NEEDED:

An empty tin can of 4" - 5" diameter, or larger.

An ordinary spring mouse trap

A piece of hardware cloth (heavy screen) about 6" X 6"

Small nails and pieces of soft wire or raveling from a wire
screen.

HOW TO MAKE:

Flatten the tin can slightly on
one side, so that it will
stand without rolling. At
the open end of the can,
nail or wire the spring
mousetrap at the flattened
edge, with the half of the
trap containing the spring
extending outside the tin
can, and with the half of
the trap with the trigger,
inside the can.

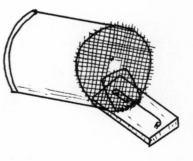

Cut a circle of hardware cloth about 1" greater in diameter than the tin can. Trim one edge flat to fit the surface of the mousetrap, and wire the hardware cloth to the spring part of the mousetrap.

Cut a small hole in the hardware cloth (see illustration), just outside the spring of the mousetrap. This is for the wire which is placed beneath the trigger when the trap is set.

Bait the trap with peanut butter, cheese, or oatflakes and set it in the woods or fields. When a small animal touches the bait, the trap will spring shut behind it.

Be certain to mark the location where traps are set, and to visit them at least twice a day, preferably morning and evening. If a trap is set in the open, protect it from the sun which could raise the temperature inside a tin can trap to a point where animals caught in the trap might suffer considerably.

A TRAP-DOOR TRAP

This trap is very simple in operation, though it may appear a bit difficult to construct. It features a trap-door balanced on a trigger. When an animal enters the baited trap, it releases the trap-door which falls closed behind it, making it impossible for the animal to get out.

A very simple trap may be made with a trap-door which remains closed until an animal pushes it open to reach the bait, then finding the trap-door has fallen shut behind it.

MATERIALS NEEDED:

1 piece hardware cloth (heavy screening) 9" X 11" or larger

1 piece hardware cloth 3" X 3"

1 piece thin sheet aluminum or tin about 3" X 3"

1 piece thin sheet aluminum or tin about 3" X 3-1/2"

Tin Shears

Pliers

About 8" soft wire

HOW TO MAKE:

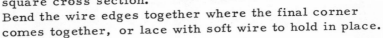

Shape the hardware cloth
    into a long box by
    bending to form a
    square cross section.
    Bend the wire edges together where the final corner
    comes together, or lace with soft wire to hold in place.

Cut the smaller piece of hardware cloth to fit one end of the
    box and bend wires or lace in place to hold.

The smaller piece of metal is used to make the trap-door
    for the front of the trap.   Trim this piece with the tin
    shears to about 1/4" narrower than the front entrance
    of the trap, and about 1/4" longer than the verticle
    measurement of the front entrance.   Shape and bend as
    illustrated, bending downwards at "A".

Run a wire through the two
    tabs, and fasten about
    1/4" from the top of the
    front of the trap.   The
    trap-door should open in-
    wards so as to fall to a
    closed position after an
    animal enters and the trap
    is sprung.

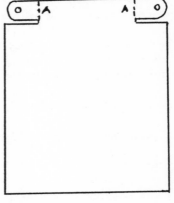

The larger piece of sheet met-
    al is used to make the
    trigger of the trap.   The
    width of the trigger should
    be about 1/4" less than
    the width of the trap, or
    the same width as the trap-door.

Cut and bend to shape as illustrated. (Bend downwards at
the broken lines lettered "A", and upwards at "B".

Two small tabs are cut and bent downwards between the
center and front of the trigger and holes punched in the
tabs, through which a wire is run to attach the trigger
to the sides of the trap. This wire acts as a hinge on
which the trigger moves.

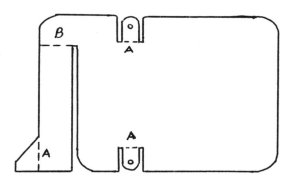

A cut is made, part of the way across the front of the trigger,
leaving a strip about 5/8" wide as illustrated. This
strip is bent upwards at right angles to the bed of the
trigger (B in illustration). At the end of this strip there
is a small projection to be bent downwards (A in illustration). Each bend is a right angle.

To locate the position of the trigger inside the trap, open the
trap-door and place the trigger so that the upright strip
holds the door in an open position when the back of the
trigger is raised, but allows the door to drop to a closed
position when the back of the trigger is lowered.

When the position for the trigger has been determined, run
a wire through the tabs which have been bent downwards
on the bottom of the trigger, and attach the wire to the
sides of the trap, about 1/8" from the bottom of the trap.

HOW TO USE:

Set the trap by opening the door and raising the back of the
trigger so that the upright strip will hold the trap-door
open. Add bait, such as oat flakes, peanut butter, or
cheese, on the inside and at the rear of the trap. As
an animal enters to reach the bait, it will step on the
trigger, and the trap-door will fall shut behind it.

Set the trap in the woods or open fields and remember to
visit the trap regularly, and at least twice each day.

A FIGURE FOUR TRAP

One of the oldest types of traps is called the Figure Four
Trap, and is a comparatively simple and easily made device,
requiring but three pieces of wood, a jackknife, box, and
bait.

This type of trap has been used to trigger a deadfall design-
ed to kill the animal which trips it, but we shall modify it
into a trap for catching small wild animals alive, for study
and possible addition to our camp zoo. These animals might
be such as rabbit, woodchuck, coon, porcupine, or skunk.
Be very careful in handling trapped animals of this size,
always wearing gloves, and transfering them quickly to a
suitable cage while they are being observed. Never keep a
wild animal for more than three or four days however.

MATERIALS NEEDED:

Three pieces of softwood of the following approximate sizes-
    18" X 1" X 3/4"
    15" X 1" X 3/4"
    12" X 1" X 3/4"

A sharp jackknife

A fairly large wooden or metal box

HOW TO MAKE:

Take a good look at the illustration. There are three pieces
labeled A, B, and C.

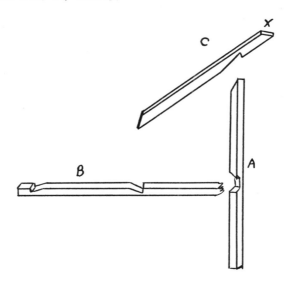

A is the upright leg of the figure four. The bottom end
should be sharpened for driving into the ground.

The other end of A is beveled to a point. On one side of
piece A, and at a point about half way between the two
ends, another beveled point is cut half way through the
stick, and with the bevel on the same edge of the stick
as is the bevel at the end of the stick.

Piece B has two notches cut into the same side. The first
notch is about one inch from one end; and the second
notch about 6" from the first notch. The first notch
has its verticle edge towards the end of the stick while
the verticle edge of the second notch faces in the opposite direction.

The unnotched end of this stick is whittled to a point to hold
the bait.

Piece C must be cut to fit the figure four shape of the trap, with its length depending on the other two pieces all ready cut. Bevel the bottom end to a point as illustrated.

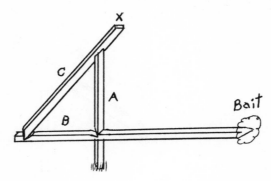

To locate the position for the notch at the other end of piece C, assemble the pieces as in the illustration. The notch on the under side of the upper end of piece C is located at the point where it will hold piece B in a position parallel to the ground. Point X at the end of piece C should be cut to also be parallel to the ground when the trap is set.

HOW TO USE:

Test the trap several times to make sure that it operates correctly. Set a wooden box upside down, with the center edge of one end resting on the top of the figure four at the point X in the illustration, and over the bait. The weight of the box should hold the trap in a set position.

If the trap works as it should, any slight tugging at the bait should spring the trap and allow the box to drop, capturing whatever animal is at the bait. If the trap does not spring easily, trim the corresponding notches of pieces A and B until the slightest tugging at the bait springs the trap.

For bait, use lettuce, carrots, old meat, etc., depending upon the animal you may be trying to capture. Tie the bait to the trigger, or force the point of the trigger into the bait.

TRAPPING WITH A CAMERA

Many animals and birds have no part in the camp zoo, nor
are they easy to trap, yet they are just as interesting as
those we can trap, and are as much a part of our nature
education. These we can try to trap with a camera, with
the camera so arranged that the subject takes its own picture. Some of these pictures will become a most interesting
part of your nature program.

MATERIALS NEEDED:

A flash camera having a lever to trip the shutter

Heavy black thread or cord

A spring mouse trap

Heavy cord, plastic tape, or other material to anchor the
    camera and trap

Bait

Some form of protection for the camera

HOW TO ARRANGE:

Select a location where some animal is apt to pass, and
    where the camera may be attached to a tree or post and
    focused on the spot where the bait is to be placed.

Fasten the camera in position, using heavy cord, plastic
    tape, friction tape, or other material to hold the cam-
    era in place.

Determine the area covered by the camera lens and mark
    this spot as the place for the bait.

Just below the camera, and in line with the shutter release,
    fasten the spring mouse trap to the tree or post, with
    the spring part of the trap on the side of the trap farthest
    away from the camera when the trap is in a sprung
    position.

50

Tie a piece of black thread to the spring of the trap with the
other end attached to the shutter release of the camera.
Adjust the thread so that when the trap is sprung, the
shutter release is pulled just far enough to open the
shutter and set off the flash. Make certain the thread
is not too short and apt to damage the camera by pulling
the shutter release too far.

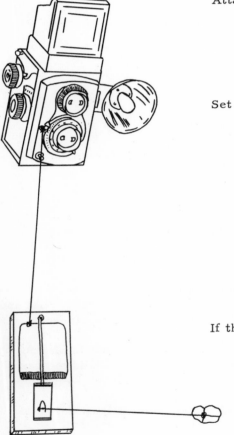

Attach a second thread to the
trigger of the mouse trap,
with the thread just long
enough to tie to the bait at
the spot selected and
marked.

Set the trap and camera and
test the set-up several
times by tugging at the
bait so as to snap the trap
which in turn should snap
the camera. When you
are certain that it works
properly, load the camera
with film and flashbulb
and place the bait in the
selected spot. Whatever
animal touches the bait
during the day or night
should take its own picture.

If the camera is to be left out
over night, wrap it in
plastic or otherwise pro-
tect it from dew and pos-
sible rain. Be sure to
leave the lens uncovered.

Use bait for the animal desired. Think of what that animal
would like, and bait the trap accordingly. Meat might
appeal to a fox, skunk, or coon; corn to a coon or skunk;
lettuce or cabbage to a rabbit; fish or honey to a coon or

bear; salt to a deer. Some of the lures used in trapping may be added to the bait if desired. These will help to bring certain animals from a further distance away.

CAGES FOR AN INSECT ZOO

In the book, "Creative Nature Crafts", we discussed the creation of an insect zoo, and also included some ideas for housing the insects in the zoo. Here are other types that may be added to the cages for the zoo.

A CORK-PIN CAGE FOR CRICKETS

In China, crickets have been kept in tiny cages made of straw or bamboo since ancient times. Here is a similar type made from pieces of cork and a few pins. It may be used for other small insects as well as for crickets.

HOW TO MAKE:

Cut thin slices from the top of a large cork, using a very sharp knife or razor blade, or a cake knife with a serrated (sawtooth) edge.

Push a row of pins through one slice of cork to make the top of the cage, keeping the pins about 1/8" from the edge of the cork, and a about the same distance apart. Push the pins all of the way through the top piece of cork, and just far enough into the bottom cork to hold well.

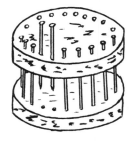

Leave two or three of the pins part way out, making a gate to put the insect through, and then push those pins into place to shut the gate.

52

Such a cage is only for insects on exhibit, and should not be used to keep them in permanently.

"Creative Nature Crafts" tells how to feed and keep insects, or this information may be found in any good insect book.

A HOUSE FOR CRICKETS

Crickets are interesting to keep, watch, and care for, and will live for a long time with little care.

Let's make a cricket house from an old flower pot, a glass lamp chimney, some cheese cloth and some soil.

HOW TO MAKE:

The glass chimney is set firmly into soil in the flower pot, and a small piece of cheesecloth is tied over the open end of the chimney.

Feed the cricket on tiny pieces of bread, lettuce, and other greens. Add a little moisture to the soil occasionally, and do not leave food in the cage until it spoils.

Watch your cricket and see how he calls for for you by scraping his wing covers.

A HOME FOR POLLIWOGS

Polliwogs are not insects, of course, but you may want to add them to your zoo for they are most interesting.

Any kind of glass jar or container will make a good home for polliwogs. It may be a regular aquarium or an improvised one. The important thing is to see that they have the right kind of food to make them grow.

You will enjoy watching the changes that polliwogs go through to become frogs.

If your polliwogs have tails, they will need to have some of the green algae and other vegetation found in pond water. Get some of this food at the same time that you collect your polliwogs.

When the polliwogs start growing legs, they also start to become insect eaters, particularly liking flies and mosquitoes, including the larvae of the mosquito. They will also want some small rocks on which to climb at this stage.

A CATERPILLAR CAGE

A cylinder of window screening 4"- 5" in diameter, laced together with a piece of wire pulled from the edge of the screening, and set into a small slab of Plaster of Paris, makes an excellent cage for caterpillars while they are preparing to pupate; or in which to keep the pupae or cocoon of a moth, or the chrysalis of a butterfly.

If caterpillars are collected, also collect daily, some of the same food plant on which the caterpillar was found. They will need this food as long as they are actively eating.

Most caterpillars mature in 4 - 5 weeks. Collect the larger ones as they are usually more mature and will start spinning a cocoon or changing to a chrysalis sooner.

Keep daily watch of your caterpillar and you will see the miraculous changes through which it goes in changing to a moth or butterfly. Watch him spin his cocoon, or hang himself by a silken thread as he goes into the chrysalis stage.

When he emerges as a butterfly or moth, watch him unpack and dry his wings, for they have been packed almost like a parachute in its case. The wings will gradually straighten and strengthen and soon he will be ready to fly, a completely

different creature than the one you placed in the cage only a
few weeks before.   If he is not to be added to your mounted
insect collection, let him go before he beats his wings to
pieces on the sides of the cage.

GROWING THINGS

Things are constantly growing all around us, but they grow so slowly, and so much of the growth is hidden, that we often do not know just how growth occurs.

Let's set up a few demonstrations that show how this growth does occur.

SEEING SEEDS GROW

Make a small box with one side being of glass, slid into slots cut into the sides of the boards, about 1/4" from the edges. Fill the box with soil or vermiculite, and plant three or four large seeds (beans, corn, peas) in the soil next to the glass where they can be observed. Provide a dark paper, cloth, or cardboard with which to cover the glass, but which may be removed occasionally to see what has occurred.

Keep the soil moist but not wet, and in a warm place. Germination will soon take place.

Remove the dark cloth or paper once each day and observe what new changes have taken place as germination and growth go on.

WATCHING SLIPS AND TWIGS TAKE ROOT

Twigs of willow, forsythia, ivy, and many other plants, shrubs, and trees, will take root in a glass of water.

Try several different kinds and observe each
day how much root development has occurred.
Place them in a glass of water and stand them
in a warm place at room temperature. Little
light is needed but will usually do no harm
either. Water will evaporate and needs to be
replaced occasionally.

HOW BULBS DEVELOP INTO PLANTS

Some plants develop by both bulbs and
seeds.

Take an onion or narcissus bulb and set
it on the top of an ink bottle filled with
water. Soon roots will develop and
growth will start at the top of the bulb.
Watch and see which comes first, and
how much occurs from day to day.

SOME PLANTS START FROM ROOTS

Some plants can grow either from seeds, or from roots
which have remained in the soil over winter, or which have
been stored and then replanted in the spring. Two of these
are carrots and parsnips. Can you name others?

We can see how they develop by placing a parsnip or a carrot in a dish of water. Growth will soon start and there will be a beautiful bouquet of greenery at the top of the carrot or parsnip.

Try a sweet potato in the same way. It makes a very attractive vine.

Or cut the end off a fairly large carrot; hollow out the center; push two wires through the end of the carrot and attach strings for hanging. Fill the hollowed out center with water and watch the carrot grow. Green shoots will grow from the top of the carrot, curling up around the bottom of the carrot towards the light.

WATCHING GRASS GROW

Place a sponge in a shallow dish of water and sprinkle grass seed over the top of the sponge. It will soon be covered with growing grass.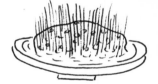

We have been watching things grow, and have learned some of their growing habits. Every growing thing needs food. Those plants or seeds that are growing in soil will grow much better and be much stronger than those growing in water alone, for most plants get their food from the soil.

Can you think of plants that do not get their food from the soil? How do they grow?

MAKING A SCIENCE OBSERVATION MOUNT

THE RIKER MOUNT

A Riker Mount is an easily made mounting box for the display and study of insects, leaves, minerals, life histories, etc.

MATERIALS NEEDED:

A shallow box such as a hosiery box. If several mounts are to be made, all of the boxes should be of the same shape and size for best appearance.

Cotton batting

Surgical cotton

Glass or heavy plastic

Gummed plastic or cloth tape, about 1" wide

HOW TO MAKE:

Mark a 1/2" border around the top of the box. Using a sharp knife, scissors, or safety razor blade, cut along this line, removing the center section of the top.

Cut the glass or heavy plastic to a size to fit the inside of the top and fasten it in place with tape.

Fill the bottom of the box with cotton batting, covering this with a thin layer of surgical cotton which is much whiter than the cotton batting, making a better background.

- 58 -

Place the materials to be mounted, on the cotton; replace
the cover; and fasten the cover in place with tape.
Labels may be placed either inside the mount; on the
outside of the cover; or on the underside of the mount,
depending upon their use.

CRAFTS USING NATIVE MATERIALS

We have been taking a look at growing things, both plant and animal, and have been using nature activity crafts in our study of both forms of life.

Now let's make use of some of the products of living things in our crafts program, not only for what we can create, but to help us appreciate still more the importance of nature. Let's remember, too, that nature is not made entirely of growing things. In the following crafts, we will be using inanimate materials from nature, as well as those that were once parts of living things.

NATIVE CLAYS

We do not know when clay was first used, but we do know that long before recorded time began, man learned that he could mold wet clay, and that he could harden it with heat. It is one of the most ancient of crafts as indicated by the Bible and by the work of archeologists.

Even the word "ceramics" used to designate many crafts made from clay, has an ancient derivation, coming from the Greek work "keramos" for potter's clay. It may also have a relationship with the Latin word, "cremare" meaning "to burn". These would seem logical, for ceramics are materials made from potter's clay, and then are burned or fired.

Clay is one of the most universally obtained craft materials, being as near as the "out-of-doors". Usually we find it mixed with other soils and so it must be cleaned of those soils before using.

To determine whether soil has a clay content, squeeze a handful of slightly moist soil. If it sticks together and retains the imprints of the fingers, it has some clay content.

HOW TO OBTAIN AND PREPARE CLAY FOR USE:

Hunt for beds of clay along the nearest stream bank. It will
show as a yellow, brown, reddish, or gray colored soil
without definite granular structure or grain. When
moist it has a slippery soapy feel. When dry it becomes
very hard, but may be powdered quite easily.

Gather the desired quantity and clean it, a half pail at a time.

Stir 1/2 pail of water into 1/2 pail of clay and strain into a
third container. Do this several times, and after the
third or fourth time, strain through a double thickness
of cheesecloth. Do this straining several times also.

The clay which we want, is the material which goes through
the cheesecloth and gives the water its cloudy or milky
appearance. Save this water and let the suspended clay
settle to the bottom; then pour off the water, saving the
clay.

As soon as the clay is dry enough, work it with the hands,
to get rid of air bubbles. Air in the clay causes small
explosions when clay objects are being fired in a kiln.
This work is usually done on a plaster bat or board,
made of Plaster of Paris. This board should be made
in advance and is about one foot square by two inches
thick.

To make the plaster bat, construct a tin or wooden form,
12" X 12" X 2". Mix enough Plaster of Paris to a
creamy consistency, to fill the form; allow the plaster
to harden; remove it from the form and let dry for several days before using.

Use this plaster bat to knead the moist clay. Occasionally
take a knife and cut through the clay mass. If there
are any air holes evident, the clay requires more knead-
ing before being used.

USING NATIVE CLAYS:

Most native clays will harden better if 1 tablespoon of dex-
trin (from a science supply house) or Dexin (baby food)
is added to each pound of clay.   This should be added
before the clay is kneaded on the plaster bat.

When the clay has been properly prepared, it should be
stored moist, in a plastic bag until used.

Clays may be molded with the hands; used on a potter's
wheel; or used in slabs or coils.

Slabs and coils are probably the most common use in camp-
crafts.

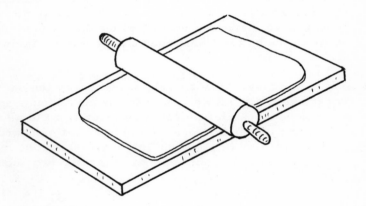

To make slabs, roll the clay to a uniform thickness using a rolling pin
on a flat surface.   Cut the slab of
clay into the proper sizes for box
sides, bottom, and top, using a
sharp knife and a ruler or other
straight edge.   Put the cut slabs
together, moistening the clay at
the edges where they join, using
a creamy mixture of clay and wa-

ter. Let the finished product dry thoroughly, when it can be fired in a kiln, or painted "as is" if desired.

Coils are often used for making vases, pitchers, etc.

To make a coil, take a handful of the moist clay and roll it beneath the palm of the hand on a hard smooth surface. It will form into long cylindrical shapes. These should be rolled to a uniform thickness of about 1/4". Make them into vase shapes by coiling the rolls of clay to make the bottom of the vase, and then placing one coil on top of another to build up the sides of the vase into the desired shape and size.

Each coil of clay should have a diagonal cut at the end, to assure a good fit where another piece is joined to it. To make the best joints, brush a little of the creamy clay and water mixture (called slip) over each joining.

To keep the vase in the desired shape, cut a template from cardboard before starting to mold the vase. This is a cut-out of the outline of the shape of the vase, and is used by placing it next to the mold as it is built up, to check on its shape.

The final step is to complete the vase by smoothing both the outsides and the insides with the fingers and palms of the hands, keeping them moistened with water.

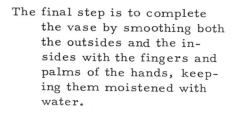

When the vase has dried enough to stand handling, turn it upside down, and gouge a 1/16" to 1/8" depression in the
center of the vase, leaving an outside flat ring of about
1/4" in diameter. As a vase dries and as it is fired in
a kiln, it has a tendency to warp. Making this depression will help to assure a more even base so that the
vase will stand erect.

Material on firing and glazing may be found in other publications, some of which are listed in the bibliography at the
end of this book. Much of the clay crafts done in camps,
however, is decorated "as is" when the clay has dried suf-
ficiently, and is not glazed or fired.

INDIAN PAINTS

Back in the Indian days there were no paint stores. When
an Indian wanted to paint, he had to start from scratch and
make his own paints, but there is no secret in how it was
done, and today, any person can make his own paints and
do his own decorating using Indian designs and motifs.

HERE'S HOW:

Every part of the country has its "paint stones". These are
any colored stones that are soft enough to make a mark on
wood or paper. These paint stones are called "pigments".

To collect your own paint stones or pigments, try out the
soft stones in your area that will pass the test of marking
in color on paper or wood.

Here are some that you can be certain of finding:

>   Clays - there is a wide range of soft colors, ranging
>   from browns, yellows, and greys, through terra
>   cotta, purple, and even blue.

>   Iron Ores - soft rocks with an earthy red color

Chalk, gypsum, limestone, white clay - these are used with other pigments to make a lighter color.

Carbon - charcoal and soot, used as black or mixed with other colors to make them darker.

A great many colors are not needed. Most Indians used a range of three colors only; one being dark and rich, used for outlining, usually a black, dark brown, or dark blue; one a color of middle value, a medium red, brown or terra cotta; and one a light color, white or yellow. The color of the background material adds a fourth color.

Using three colors only helps to stimulate the imagination and leads to the development of blended colors and rhythm of design.

MATERIALS NEEDED:

Fine wire screening

Jars or other containers for storing pigments

Wooden mallet for pounding soft stones into powdered pigments

Heavy plastic or cloth bags in which pigments are pounded to a powder

Newspapers to protect tables or workbenches during pounding

Smooth stones for the final grinding of the pigments to a fine powder

Mucilage.

HOW TO PREPARE:

Break the collected soft stones and clays into as small pieces as possible before powdering them. Be sure that the clays are absolutely dry.

Place the small pieces in a small plastic bag
and pound them to a powder with a wooden
mallet.

After pounding, grind the small pieces remaining, to a very fine powder, using two smooth
stones as a mortar and pestle for grinding.

Sift through a very fine sieve or cheesecloth, and
store the dry pigments in jars.

When ready to use the pigments as paint, mix
only as much as needed at the time.

Add water to the dry pigment until it has the consistency of heavy cream and then stir in one
teaspoonful of mucilage for each pint of paint.
The mucilage is what makes the paint stick
and the amount needed will vary with different
pigments. Try out the paint. If it rubs off
too easily when it has dried, more mucilage
should be added.

NOW LET'S PAINT:

These "Earth Paints" have many uses, depending upon the program of the group making them.

Learn some of the Indian signs and symbols. In
your local library, look for books of Indian
Crafts from which to select designs, or make up
designs for yourself.

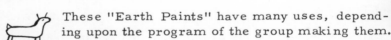

Two of the books which you might find extremely

useful are these:

> "The Golden Book of Indian Crafts and Lore", by Ben
> Hunt, and published by Simon and Schuster, 630
> Fifth Ave., New York 20, N.Y.

> "The Book of Indian Crafts and Indian Lore", by Julian
> H. Salomon, published by Harper Brothers, 49 E.
> 33rd St., New York 16, N.Y.

Use a regular paint brush and try out these paints in decorating your own Indian teepee made from an old sheet, or
for decorating a model Indian village.

Use them too, on Indian head-dresses, and on rattles, shirts,
trousers, etc. They may be used for war-paints for Indian
plays or pageants, by mixing the pigments with lanolin.

Some of the Indian designs you might like to use border the
preceding page.

JUICE PAINTS

In addition to the "Earth Pigments", nature is well stocked
with colors, especially in the fall. These colors can be
rewarding, when used on rough drawing paper which will
help extract the colors.

Colors are extracted by briskly rubbing the moist leaf, flower, or stem, on drawing paper.

What colors are there? You may find that some things will
give unexpected colors.

While collecting materials for juice painting, make up a
chart of the colors to be found by trying each out on a piece
of drawing paper. Keep these sample colors on hand when
you are painting, so that you can use the correct material
to obtain the needed color. Be sure that your samples are
labeled.

Red flowers do not always produce red color, nor are greens always from green colored materials. Purple flowers may give a brown color, or even orange. Leaves and blades may give a different color than the stems.

Rotten wood may give a brownish-red paint color.

Try out leaves, stems, blades, mosses, flowers, fruit skins, berries, clays, and soft stones. Try adding white sticky juices such as milkweed juice, using them to hold powdered mica or sand on parts of your pictures.

MAKE A STARCH PAINT

For a thick paint made of native materials use a liquid starch base.

MATERIALS NEEDED:

Bottle of liquid starch

Small containers for each color of paint

Crushed leaves, moss, wood dust, clay, flowers, berries, charcoal, etc.

Small paint brushes or cotton swabs

HOW TO MAKE:

In small amounts of liquid starch, mix well each of the crushed or powdered materials which have been collected for their color.

Use each color of paint, applying it to your design with a paint brush or cotton swab.

NATURAL DYES

Berries, barks, stems, and even flowers of some plants
provide beautiful colors. These natural dyes always produce
soft colors that blend well and are a pleasing contrast to the
brilliant hues of commercial dyes.

The pleasure of preparing and using natural dyes is the satisfaction of doing the entire job for oneself.

There are a few general rules that we should follow in ex-
tracting and using dyes from natural materials.

1- Steep the plants, leaves, berries, stems, or nuts,
   in water overnight and then boil them slowly for an
   hour or more until the desired intensity of color is
   obtained, usually much more concentrated than the
   shade desired in the material to be dyed.

2- An enameled kettle is most desirable in dying. It
   should be large enough to hold both the needed amount
   of dye plus the material to be dyed.

3- Use wooden paddles or spoons for stirring the dyes
   and handling the materials being dyed.

4- Material to be dyed should first be washed with soap
   and water, and then thoroughly rinsed.

5- Many materials will not take dyes well, and will fade
   easily unless first treated with a mordant, a chemi-
   cal which will help the material to take the color,
   and to hold it well afterwards.

   Prepare a mordant by dissolving powdered alum in
   water at the rate of one ounce of alum to one gallon
   of water. After the materials have been washed and
   rinsed well, immerse them in this mordanting solution, boil slowly for about one hour, remove and
   rinse well, and then place the material in the dye
   bath.

Animal fibers such as wool and silk, should have 1/4 ounce of Cream of Tartar added to each gallon of alum water in the mordant bath.

Vegetable fibers such as cotton, linen, and rayon, need 1/4 ounce of regular washing soda added to each gallon of the alum water in the mordant solution.

6- Boil the material in the dye for from 1/2 to 1 hour, then add 1 tablespoon of salt, or 1/2 cup of vinegar and boil for 10 to 15 minutes longer.

7- Remove from the dye, rinse, and dry in a shaded place.

WHAT COLORS ARE THERE?

The following natural materials will provide dyes in the colors indicated, and in varying intensities.

RED -

Onion skins (red)	Alder (inner bark)
Pokeberries (the berries)	Beets
Raspberries	Amaranth (seeds)
Red Dogwood (inner bark)	Strawberries
Blood-root	

ORANGE -

Mountain-ash (berries)	Amaranth (flowers)

YELLOW -

Onion skins (yellow)	Tanglewood (stems)
Goldenrod (plant and flowers)	Citron
Pear leaves	Sassafras (bark)

Sumac leaves

Sumac roots

Celladine

GREEN -
Elderberry leaves

Spinach leaves

BLUE -
Larkspur flowers

Sunflower seeds

PURPLE -
Blueberries

Barberry (berries)

Staghorn Sumac (berries)

MAGENTA -
Dandelion roots

PINK -
Sassafras roots

BROWN -
Butternut (shells and bark)

Staghorn Sumac (bark)

Maple (bark)

Alder (bark)

GREY -
Staghorn Sumac (leaves)

Butternut (bark)

St. John's wort (flowers)

Cottonwood (leaf buds)

Lichens

Arbor Vitae leaves

Water algae

Blackberries

Pokeberry (stems)

Elderberries

Cedar berries

Walnut (shells and bark)

Hickory (bark)

Red Oak (bark)

Maple (bark)

BLACK -
Maple (inner bark and leaves)

Field Sorrel (leaves)

Staghorn Sumac (leaves and berries)

SEED PAINTING

Use colored seeds and cement in place of paints? Yes, you can, and with very interesting results, too. They can be used to paint a picture; to decorate a picture frame; and even to make symbols such as Indian and Scout designs.

Get a supply of several of the larger varieties of dried seeds, such as corn, peas, beans of various sizes and colors, rice, lentils, squash, and pumpkin, muskmelon, and others. You will also need household cement and heavy paper or cardboard for the background.

Draw or trace the desired design on the background material, marking in the colors to be used. (These should be the same as the colors of the seeds which you have on hand.) Use the darker seeds, such as red kidney beans, or red corn, for the outlines.

Apply a small amount of cement to the back of a seed and cement it in place, doing the outlines first, and then adding seeds of other colors to fill in the rest of the picture.

FUNGUS PICTURES

Towards the end of the summer, one often sees large shelf fungi growing on the trunk of a tree, or an a fallen log. These are dark on the top but have a light colored undersurface having an interesting characteristic. The slightest pressure on this light colored under-surface will make a mark that is permanent. Since we are interested in this characteristic, we must take care in gathering the fungus for craft use.

Place a soft cloth against the underside of the fungus while it is being pried from the tree or log, and being carried back to the camp or home.

Plan your drawing be-
fore transferring it to
the fungus. With any
moderately sharp point-
ed instrument such as a
pencil, ice pick, etc.,
draw the picture on the
light side of the fungus.
Each mark made, will
turn brown and will re-
main permanently.

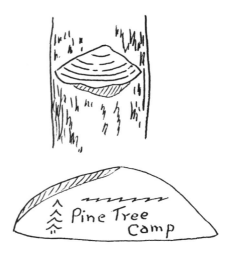

Trim or saw the thick
edge of the fungus so it
will stand in the desired
position, and then shel-
lac the dark surfaces of
fungus, using several
coats of shellac and dry-
ing well between coats. Do not shellac the light surface
where the drawing has been made.

BASKET MAKING MATERIALS

Many of the materials used for basket making are of foreign origin, including raffia, bamboo, hemp, reed, and rattan, but in our country we have willow, straw, cattail leaves, rushes, flags; grasses such as sweet grass, sedges, broom grass, wire grass, and orchard grass; vines such as Virginia Creeper and honeysuckle; barks such as moosefoot maple, basswood, and elm; tree root fibers such as hemlock and spruce; plant stems like maidenhair fern, and Indian hemp; wood splints of hickory, black ash, white ash, oak, and maple; and a number of other materials used locally includ-ing corn husks, and long pine needles.

PREPARATION OF MATERIALS:

Fine willow branches, known as osiers, are gathered in the
    spring.   These are usually from 1/8" to 3/16" in diam-
    eter.   The bark is removed and the bare shoots are the
    parts used in basket making.

Vines such as Virginia Creeper and honeysuckle should be
    two years old before using.   The bark is removed by
    scraping, or by pulling the vine through a small V-
    shaped hole in the end of a small piece of wood that will
    fit the hand.   The vines without the bark, are well soak-
    ed in water before using in basket making.

Wood splints are pounded from logs that have been soaked in
    a pond or lake for at least a month, to loosen the fibers
    from each other.

    Remove the outer bark.   With a heavy mallet or the
    back of a single bitted axe, pound the length of the log
    until a strip of the wood is loosened.   It will require
    considerable pounding, but must not be done so hard as
    to damage the wood.   When a strip is loosened, start a
    strip at one end of the log with a knife or hand axe, and
    peel it for the full length of the log.   The strip will vary
    in thickness from 1/16" to 1/8", and will also vary in
    width.

    Remove all of the strips that have been loosened, and
    then pound loose a second layer.   When necessary, re-
    volve the log, and pound and peel strips from the other
    side.   The heartwood of the log will not make good
    splints, but is fine for other uses requiring a tough hard
    wood.

Gather cattails and rushes when they are immature and dry
    them slowly to keep them from getting brittle.

Corn husks may be dried in the sun or shade.   Those dried
    in the sun will bleach almost white, while those dried
    in the shade will remain a delicate green.   The outer
    husks are rather coarse while the inner ones next to the
    ear, are soft and fine.

Long pine needles are picked green and dried in the sun or shade. Those dried in the sun will turn a golden brown while those dried in the shade will remain a light green. Pine needles may also be used without drying.

Grasses may be gathered while they are green, and then dried, or the dry grasses may be gathered in the fall. If they are brittle, be sure to soak them well before using.

PINE NEEDLE CRAFTS

The needles of both the Long-leaf Pine and the Slash Pine are excellent for craft use. Where these pines are available, they often have needles growing nearly a foot in length.

A PINE NEEDLE BROOM

Gather the needles of one of the above varieties of pine and allow them to dry in the sun for a few days, then pull the bunches of needles apart separating them into the individual needles.

HOW TO MAKE:

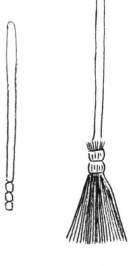

Obtain an old broom stick or a 3/4" dowel, and cut three notches around one end, 1" apart and with the first notch about 1" from the end of the stick.

Gather a handful of the pine needles; arrange them evenly around the bottom notch of the handle and tie them tightly in place with a strong cord. Do the same at both the second and third notches, tying the needles tightly in place.

Trim the pine needles evenly at the bottom of the broom,
and just above the tie at the third notch and the broom
is completed.

A PINE NEEDLE BRUSH

Gather and dry long pine needles as directed in the above
article. Select a large number of needles approximately the
same length.

HOW TO MAKE:

Gather 30 - 35 needles in a bunch and tie them tightly about
4" from the pointed end of the needles. Gather another
bunch of the same number of needles. Place them
against the first bundle with the ends about 1/4" from
the ends of the first bunch. Tie them to the first bunch
of needles at a point 1/4" above where that bunch is tied.

Continue with 15 to 20
bunches of needles,
tying each bunch to
the previous bunches
of needles, 1/4" a-
bove the previous
tie. Be certain that
each added bunch of
needles is placed in line with the previous bunches so
that the finished brush will have all of its "bristles" in
a straight line on the same side of the brush.

When there is but about 4" left at the handle end of the first
bunch of needles, wrap and tie all of the needles at this
point, trimming off the ends of the longer needles,
making a handle for the brush. The handle at this point
should be about one inch in diameter. Wrap it tightly,
and if needed, shellac the handle to hold the wrapping
and needles in place.

A final wrapping of raffia gives a neat appearance to the
handle of the brush.

Trim the ends of the needles evenly and you have a fine
clothes brush or whisk broom. It is very durable.

A CORN HUSK BRUSH

A good corn husk brush may be made, essentially as directed
above under "A Pine Needle Brush", but will require a wood-
en handle.

HOW TO MAKE:

Obtain a handle, perhaps from an old broom, or a 3/4"
dowel, about 12" long.

Cut 5 notches around one end of the handle, starting 1"
from the end, and with the notches 1" apart.

Use the outside husks of the corn for the most durable
brush, or the inner husks for a softer and finer brush.

Take ten strips of husk about 3/4" wide, and bind them
tightly around the handle at the first notch, 4" from the
ends of the husks.

At the second notch, tie ten more strips of husk, placing
just enough of the husks at the upper side to cover the
handle, and the rest on the under side of the brush.
Tie them 4" from the ends of the husks as before.

Do the same procedure again, tying at the third notch, etc.
until husks have been added at each of the five notches.

When the final group of husks has been tied in place, wrap
the remaining part of the handle with heavy cord or raffia, and trim the bottom of the brush evenly.

The husks may be dyed, and the handle may be carved if
desired. If it is to be carved, it should be made from
soft pine, a stick of green witchhazel, or some other
easily carved wood.

Add a thong through the handle, for hanging.

BIRCH—BARK CRAFTS

For the Indian, the bark of the white birch took the place of leather, paper, canvas, and tin. He found abundant uses for this natural material which is almost indestructible excepting by fire. It is both thick and thin; insect and decay proof; and even waterproof. It made his canoes, roof, fire tinder, baskets, bottles, and cooking pots.

There were other useful barks such as basswood, spruce, and hemlock, cedar, and elm, but none that had as many uses as the white birch bark.

GETTING THE BARK:

> NOTE: Living trees should never be stripped of their bark promiscuously. Get your supply from trees that have fallen or that are to be cut. Fallen logs that have almostly decayed may still have large pieces of bark in excellent condition.

The best bark comes from the older and larger trees. That on young trees is usually too thin. Completely removing the bark from young trees will invariably kill them, while sizeable pieces may be taken from older trees without serious damage excepting to the appearance of the tree. New bark will grow in place of the bark removed, but it will be rough and black as compared to the white bark removed from the tree.

Bark can be successfully stripped from the white birch tree only in the spring and early summer. Before removing bark from a tree, cut a tiny strip to see if the bark is thick enough for craft use. Thin bark is almost worthless, and may sometimes be found even on the older and larger trees.

To remove the bark from the tree or fresh-cut log, cut the bark in a straight line, lengthways of the trunk or log. Work the bark away from the cut with the fingers, removing it gently so as not to tear or crack the sheet being removed.

The bark may stick at the points where there are black spots or knots showing on the surface. To prevent breaking or tearing at these points, pound the area gently with a stick or the head of an axe to loosen the bark so that it can be pried away without damage.

Once the bark has been removed, roll it with the white side inside, against the natural curve of the bark, and tie the roll until ready for use.

When needed for craft use, lay the bark flat on the ground with the brown side down and weight it down to hold it flat. If it is too dry, soak it for a while in water to make it more pliable.

TOOLS NEEDED FOR BIRCH BARK CRAFTS:

Sharp knife

Tin shears

Leather punch

Ice pick or sharp-pointed awl

Glue or household cement

Darning Needle

USING THE BARK:

Birch bark may be used either side out. We may prefer the white side out for its appearance, but the brown side is the most durable and should be used for anything that is exposed to wear on the outside. Try both sides in your own crafts projects.

Pieces may be joined in a variety of ways such as overcasting with a needle and thread, yarn, raffia, or basswood cordage; they may be punched and laced; or they may be cemented and glued.

When two pieces of bark are to be laced together, small wooden pegs may be placed through holes punched in the bark, until it can be laced, after which the pegs are removed.

The edges of bark crafts may be made more durable by the addition of a wooden hoop, bound or laced with yarn, raffia, or cordage; or by binding a few strands of dried grasses, or a thin strip of cattail leaf around the edges.

At points where the bark is to be bent, place a straight edge and run the ice pick or awl along the line, making a slight crease and scoring the bark slightly, making it bend readily at this line.

Use tin shears for cutting birch bark.

Holes for lacing are punched with an ice pick or awl, using a twisting motion. If the bark tends to split, it is too dry and should be moistened.

Hoops for basket edges should be even in size throughout, and should be soaked so as to bend easily. White cedar, maple, ash, and willow make good hoops. Bend them to size and shape and bind the ends together. The hoop should go on the outside of the birch bark basket. Tie it in place temporarily; trim the bark evenly; then bind the hoop in place permanently. Holes should be punched in the bark about every 3/4" for binding. The hoop around the top of the basket should be laced in place before the final lacing of the ends of the basket to make sure of a correct fit.

Decorations on the side of birch bark crafts may be made by punching holes in a pattern, and lacing through the holes with colored yarn, raffia, cordage, or porcupine quills.

Birch bark has a tendency to curl, so where possible, place
the completed article in a press or clamp, or under
pressure of some sort until it is thoroughly dry.

BIRCH BARK BASKETS

Round baskets may be made by cutting circular pieces of
bark; slashing towards the center like cuts in a pie,
leaving the circular center part intact for the bottom of
the basket.

Bend the sections upwards; fasten temporarily with
wooden pegs or cord, and then cut a slender, pliable
shoot long enough to go around the rim, and lace or
overcast it to the outside of the rim for added strength.

Finally sew or lace the sections of the sides together.

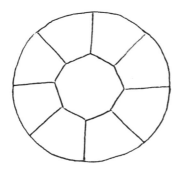

Square or rectangular baskets are made by cutting the bark
into square or rectangular shapes, slashing towards the
center at the points where the corners of the bottom are
to be located, bending the sides and ends upwards and
fastening them temporarily. A slender shoot may be
overcast or laced around the outside of the rim, bending
it carefully at the corners as it is bound in place.

Finish by sewing or lacing the edges permanently, with
yarn, raffia, or cordage.

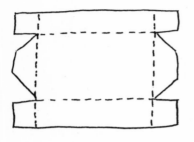

Cylindrical baskets may be
   made from a single rectangular piece of birch
   bark, overlapping and
   sewing, lacing, or gluing
   the ends.   The bottom
   may be another piece of
   birch bark, cut round to
   size, and sewed or laced
   in place.   Again lace a
   pliable shoot around the
   rim for added strength.
   The bottom may also be
   made of a piece of wood,
   cut to shape and tacked
   or glued into place.

BIRCH BARK NOVELTIES

Canoe - Draw a design as illustrated to any desired
   size.   Cut from birch
   bark and sew or lace a-
   round curved ends.   A
   pliable shoot, laced to the
   sides of the canoe gives
   added strength.

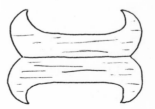

Wigwam - Cut a semicircular pattern
from heavy paper and shape like a
cone. When the desired size pattern is done, use this to cut a
piece of birch bark. Shape into a
cone and sew, lace, or glue. A
doorway may be cut out with a
sharp razor blade, and small dowels or pieces of reed glued to the
inside for tent poles. Paint with
Indian designs.

Hot Dish Mat - Cut two pieces of bark of the same shape and
size. Turn the pieces back to back (white side inside),
and with the grain of bark of one piece crossways to that
of the other piece. Sew or lace together, adding a very
small pliable shoot at the edge if desired.

Picture Frame - Cut two pieces of bark of the same size
and somewhat larger than the picture to be framed, and
with the grain of the bark running in opposite directions
to prevent curling. From one piece, cut out the center
to slightly overlap the edges of the picture being framed.
Sew or lace the edges together with either the white or
brown side out.

Napkins Rings - Use narrow strips of bark with the ends
glued together in the shape of a cylinder, and the edges
laced with yarn or raffia; or edged with dried grass and
laced.

Boxes - Use thin layers of birch bark, gluing the pieces to
small wooden boxes. Dry under a weight to prevent
curling of the bark.

Note Book - Cut pieces of
bark for the covers,
one inch larger in each
direction than the pa-
per to be used inside
the notebook. With the

brown side of the bark out, bind the edges with sweet-grass or a strip of cattail leaf, using raffia, yarn, or cordage for the lacing.

Punch holes through both birch bark and paper and tie with rawhide or raffia.

Decorate the cover with sweetgrass or raffia, laced through holes punched in the bark. Use porcupine quills for decoration if they are available.

Writing paper - Use very thin sheets of birch bark trimmed to size. It makes an excellent writing paper.

WHITTLING

Wood has been the commonest craft material for thousands of years, and whittling will continue to be popular as long as trees grow. It is a form of wood-carving using only a knife, and is easily adapted to all age groupings. It is simple and inexpensive and needs few tools for a successful experience. Actually, a jackknife with a substantial handle and a good sharp blade will produce a great many items with no other tools needed. But for more elaborate work and a good finishing job, we can use a few additional tools and pieces of equipment.

MATERIALS NEEDED:

Jackknife or other carving tool. It should be made of good steel to hold an edge, and usually has brass plates and strong springs.

A carborandum stone for sharpening tools

A coping saw, jig saw, or band saw to rough out the shapes to be whittled.

Sandpaper, both medium-coarse and very fine.

Stains or waxes

Carbon paper

Some projects will require such things as
    Household cement
    Safety- pins or pin-backs
    India ink or water colors, and pen or brush
    Linseed oil

Woods - the best woods for the beginner to whittle are the
    following:
    White Pine
    Sugar Pine
    Basswood
    Cottonwood
    Poplar
    Cedar
    Willow

And as we become more advanced, we may prefer the hard-
    woods with beautiful grain such as
    Maple
    Mahogany
    Walnut

Blocks of wood chosen for whittling should be free from
knots and cracks. Scrap wood from the local lumber yard
should provide some excellent whittling material and may
usually be had for the asking.

HOW TO WHITTLE:

First of all, learn how to sharpen your tools if you do not
    all ready know how. Do the rough sharpening on the
    coarse side of your sharpening stone, and the final
    sharpening on the fine side of the stone.

Select a pattern and a suitable block of wood large enough
    for the pattern selected. Lay a piece of carbon paper
    over the wooden block, and with a pencil trace the
    pattern onto the wood. Be sure that the grain of the
    wood runs with the main lines of the pattern. Small

parts of the pattern, running across the grain of the wood may cause the finished carving to split off at that spot. If possible use the grain of the wood to emphasize the pattern design.

Cut out the general shape of the pattern on a jig saw, or with a coping or band saw. Now you are ready to do the actual whittling.

There are two ways in which you may use the whittling knife. One is to cut away from yourself, and the other is to cut towards yourself. Cut away from yourself whenever possible. This can always be done on outside cuts. Inside cuts and the finer final cuts are usually done by cutting towards oneself, but be very careful.

Usually finish a whittled or carved object by sanding, though sometimes it is more desirable if left in the rougher whittled stage. Curved parts need a sandpaper stick. To make one, take a small dowel rod; cut a piece of fine sandpaper to fit around the rod, and cement it in place. Use this to sand the curved and inside parts of the carving.

Add eyes to animals carved. This may be done in various ways. Probably the easiest is to make an "eye punch", using a 6 penny or 8 penny nail cut or filed flat, and with a small hole drilled in the end. A light tap with a mallet will form a circle in the wood, looking very much like an eye.

Stain and wax the final carving or whittling.

WHITTLING PROJECTS

Let's start our whittling with something easy and progress from there to the more difficult whittling that requires more skill and patience.

MAKING A NAME TAG

Using small pieces of wood about 2" long, whittle a tag about 3/4" wide and with rounded edges and back.

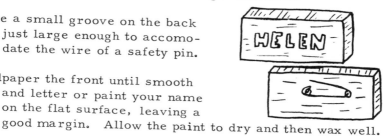

Make a small groove on the back just large enough to accomodate the wire of a safety pin.

Sandpaper the front until smooth and letter or paint your name on the flat surface, leaving a good margin. Allow the paint to dry and then wax well.

Cement the safety pin or a pin-back to the groove on the back of the tag.

MAKING A PIN

Obtain small branches of dead red cedar, oak, or other wood, about 1" in diameter.

With a small saw, cut off thin slices of the wood, either straight across or on a slant.

Sandpaper smooth, and attach a pin back as directed above.

Apply wax and polish well.

MAKING A BUTTON

Follow the same directions above,
    for making a pin, but drill
    small holes through the bot-
    tom for sewing to material,
    as illustrated.

Stain and wax as desired.

MAKING AN ANIMAL

On a sheet of paper, draw a simple outline of the animal
    selected for whittling. Cut out this outline with a pair
    of scissors, or plan to use carbon paper to transfer the
    outline to the wood.

Place the drawing or outline on the selected piece of wood
    so that the grain of the wood will be parallel to the
    weakest parts of the pattern such as legs, tail, and ears.

Transfer the outline to the wood with pencil or carbon paper.

Cut the wood along the outline with a coping saw or bandsaw,
    holding the saw vertical to the wood so that the pattern
    will come out the same on both sides.

Whittle by rounding off edges, cutting with the grain of the
    wood. The knife should be very sharp. Cut small chips
    at a time until you gain confidence that you are cutting
    in the right direction.

Don't try to carve out details; aim for general outlines.

Finish with coarse and then fine sandpaper until the wood is
    smooth and shows the beauty of the grain.

Protect the carving with a pastewax polished to a luster with
    a soft rag.

Drawings on this page and following page may be enlarged
and used for outlines, or you may draw your own.

A HIKING STICK

A good hiking stick should be just about chest high. Hickory, ash, maple, cedar, moosefoot maple, all make good hiking sticks, as do many other woods. The thickest end of the stick should be about 1" - 1-1/4" in diameter.

Saplings that have had vines growing around them, make excellent hiking sticks. Removing the vine leaves an interesting pattern pressed into the wood if the vine has been there long enough to constrict the growth of the sapling. The writer has a hiking stick made from a wild cherry sapling around which a bittersweet vine was twined, making a depression about 1/2" deep as the sapling grew. It looks very much like a snake twined around the hiking stick, and with a little help from a jackknife, a snake's head was added to give it a more striking appearance. This stick was found in a small brushlot in Virginia.

Patterns may be cut through the bark, leaving the white wood standing out aginst the darker bark; or the stick, with some of the bark removed to form a pattern, may be held over a fire until the wood is charred where the bark had been removed, after which the remaining bark is removed, leaving the design of charred wood as a deep brown pattern against the white of the uncharred part.

MAKING A NOGGIN

A noggin was the pioneer name for a wooden cup, usually made from a burl growing on the side of a tree. A burl is caused by some type of injury to the trunk of a tree, causing a growth to form on the side of the trunk. Apple and maple trees provide the best burls for craft work. When a burl in good condition has been found, and of a size large enough for a wooden cup or noggin, carefully saw it from the tree, covering the wound with paint or tar to prevent infection.

Soak the burl in water for several days, then remove the bark.

HOW TO MAKE:

You will need a good sharp knife, a gouge and mallet, a vise
and sandpaper to do the job. An augur bit or power
drill may be useful to cut away some of the unwanted
material from the inside of the noggin.

Place the burl in the vise.
Mark out the area to be
removed and drill out as
much of the wood as pos-
sible, being careful not to
drill too deep. Using the
mallet and gouge or chisel,
remove more of the wood,
working from the edges towards the center.

If the entire job is not done at
one time, soak the burl in
water between sessions.
When it is nearly done,
soak it in either raw or
boiled linseed oil between
work sessions.

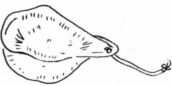

Keep a careful measurement
of the thickness of the
sides and the bottom so as
not to get them too thin.
The bottom should be a
little thicker than the sides which should be about 1/4"
thick when completed.

When the desired thickness has been achieved, finish the
noggin with a sharp knife and sandpaper, or scrape with
broken glass to smooth the inside.

Soak well with linseed oil and then polish by rubbing warm
beeswax into the bowl with a flannel cloth.

Add a leather thong, or whittle a small handle on the outside
of the noggin.

MAKING A CHESS SET

Collect a number of empty spools and use them for carving.
They are excellent for carving heads for a chess set, and
with some patience and careful planning, you can make an
excellent set of chess men, carving two sets as nearly identical as possible, and painting or staining one set, leaving
the other set in its natural color.

HOW TO MAKE:

For a complete chess set, you will need to make 32 pieces
as follows: (Make half in natural color, and the other
half stained)

16 Pawns
4 Bishops
4 Castles
4 Knights
2 Kings
2 Queens

Pawns: - Use small spools. Glue a small dowel, 1/2" long
in the hole of the spool, projecting 1/4" from the hole.

Bishops: - Glue a small spool on the top of a similar spool.
Cut a V shaped notch in the top of the upper spool.

Castles: - Use a large spool, or two spools glued together
as are the Bishops. Make right angle cuts across the
top of the spool, to look like the ramparts of a castle
(see illustration).

Knights: - Use a medium sized spool and whittle horse's
heads from soft wood and glue to the top of the spool.

Kings: - Use medi-
    um large spool
    for body. From
    a small spool
    whittle a crown
    and glue this to
    the large spool.

Queens: - Use the
    same size spool
    as for the Kings.
    Whittle a smaller
    crown from a
    small spool, and
    glue a small dow-
el in the center to help distinguish it from the Kings.

HORN CRAFTS

Cows' horns are available in many areas, especially where
there may be a local slaughter house where the horns may
usually be had for the asking. Occasionally they may be
found around a farm, or they may be purchased from a
craft supply house.

Before using them in craft programs, horns should be thoroughly cleaned and disinfected, They may be cleaned by
scraping with broken glass or a sharp knife, or even sand-
papered. Both the inside and the outside should be scraped.
After scraping, soak the horn for an hour or so in a solution
of household cleanser containing chlorine.

To make the horn easily worked, let it stand in a solution of
equal parts of water and vinegar for 36-48 hours, to soften.
When it is removed from this solution it will harden again
within a few hours.

Another method of making the horn soft is to boil it for
several hours. It will harden quickly as it cools off.

MAKE A BUGLE

MATERIALS NEEDED:

A large cow's horn

Small saw

1/4" drill

Sharp knife

Fine sandpaper

India Ink to decorate bugle

HOW TO MAKE:

Clean and disinfect the horn.

Measure the depth of the hollow part of the horn so as to locate the point where the solid part of the horn begins. Mark this point on the outside of the horn with a pencil.

Cut off the small end of the horn approximately two inches from the point marked with the pencil, leaving about a two inch solid section.

Drill a 1/4" hole lengthwise through the solid section of the horn.

With a sharp knife, cut and trim the end of the horn into the shape of a bugle mouthpiece. Smooth with sandpaper.

HOW TO USE:

Blow on your horn bugle as you would on a regular bugle.

The tone may be changed by changing the position of the lips
while blowing.

DECORATING THE HORN:

Designs may be inscribed or incised on the sides of the horn
with any sharp-pointed tool, carefully scratching the
design into the horn. When the design is completed,
India ink may be rubbed into the scratched design to
make it stand out. (This was the common way of
decorating powder horns in colonial days. Many of
these with beautiful designs may be seen in museums.)

MAKE A POWDER HORN

Powder horns are reminiscent of pioneer days and are often
found in antique shops, or hanging from the fireplace mantles
of today.

Let's make one for our own fireplace.

MATERIALS NEEDED:

Cow's horn of any size

Handsaw

1/4" drill

3/16" drill

Leather thong

Scrap pine wood

Broken glass or sharp knife

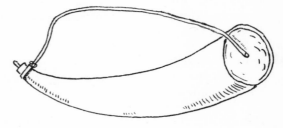

India Ink

Glue or small brads

HOW TO MAKE:

Cut the larger end of the horn square with the handsaw, and
cut off about one inch of the tip end. In the center of
the solid part of the horn where the tip was cut off,
drill a 1/4" hole through to the hollow part of the horn.

Cut a notch completely around the horn, 1/2" from the
smaller end, and carve the horn to a rounded end at
this point. The thong will be tied around the horn at
the notch.

Whittle a wooden plug to fit into the 1/4" drilled hole

From 1" pine, whittle a larger plug to fit tightly into the
large open end of the horn. Drill a 3/16" hole in the
center of this plug, thread a length of leather thong
through the hole and knot on the inside. Put the plug in
place and glue or fasten with small brads.

Tie the other end of the thong around the notch at the small
end of the horn.

Scrape the horn smooth with a sharp knife or broken glass
and polish.

If desired, scratch a design into the horn with any sharp
pointed instrument and rub India ink into the scratched
design.

MAKE A HORN CUP

Horn was the material for the frontiersman or Indian to use
in making a cup for use on the trail or at home. It was un-
breakable and light to carry, but unless the horn was very
large, the cup proved to be small in diameter, and to hold

enough, needed to be higher than it was wide, making more of a glass shape than a cup shape.

MATERIALS NEEDED:

A large horn

Sharp knife

Handsaw

Scrap pine

Waterproof glue or cement

Small brads

Linseed oil

Woolen cloth

HOW TO MAKE:

Obtain the largest horn available and cut it off squarely at the large end.

The height of the cup is determined by the straightness of the horn. With a pencil, draw a line squarely around the horn at the point selected for the top of the cup.

With the handsaw, cut almost through the horn on this line, but leaving a 1/4" thickness of the horn uncut.

With a pencil, draw a 3/4" wide strip upwards from the top of the cup, towards the tip of the horn, and starting at the uncut part. This strip will be turned down to make the handle of the cup, and should be about 5" long. Cut out the strip with a small saw, leaving the end of the strip attached to the top of the cup.

When these steps have been completed, the horn should look like the illustration on following page.

Boil the horn until it softens, then trim
down the handle to about 1/8" thick,
and narrowing from the cup to the
end of the handle.

When the handle has been thinned to
1/8" or less, boil the horn once
more until softened and quickly
bend the handle into shape. Hold
the handle in shape until the horn cools, or run cold water over it to hasten cooling and hardening, when it will
stay bent.

Make a bottom for the cup by whittling a piece of soft pine
to fit snugly at all points. Coat the edges well with
waterproof cement, put the bottom in place and attach
firmly with small brads.

Scrape, sand, and polish with linseed oil and a woolen cloth.

MAKE A HORN SPOON

A horn spoon is not difficult to make. The same materials
are needed for working the horn as listed above.

HOW TO MAKE:

With a pencil, trace the general outline of the spoon on the
outside of the horn, making it a little larger than
desired, to allow for the final trimming and finishing.

Saw the horn into half,
lengthways and then
cut out along the
pencil lines with a
coping saw, or pow-
er band or jig saw.
The large end of
the horn should form
the bowl of the spoon with the smaller end being the
handle.

Boil the horn until softened, and then trim the edges with a sharp knife. Thin the bowl and handle where necessary and give the spoon its shape by bending it while it is soft from boiling, and holding it into this shape until it cools and hardens. It may be cooled and hardened quickly by running cold water over it.

Smooth the horn by scraping with a sharp knife or broken glass, rubbing with fine sandpaper, and then polishing by rubbing with a woolen cloth moistened with linseed oil.

Decorations of scratched or incised lines may be added to the horn spoon while it is still fairly soft after boiling.

FEATHER CRAFTS

WRITING PENS OR QUILLS

Our ancesters used large quills from the wings of turkeys and geese to make their writing pens, trimming them into shape with a "pen-knife".

MATERIALS NEEDED:

Large quill (feather) from wing or tail of goose or turkey

Sand

Alum

Sharp Knife

HOW TO MAKE:

Remove the oil from the end of a large quill by placing the end of the quill in hot sand, heated in the oven. Leave the quill in the hot sand for about ten minutes, but do not place the quill in the oven.

Dissolve 1/2 teaspoonful of alum in one
cup of water and bring to a boil. Dip
the end of the quill in this solution for
about 30 seconds.

Remove from the alum solution, and
trim the quill into pen shape with a
sharp knife or razor blade. Leave
a blunt point and slit this point in the
center for about 1/2 inch to form the
two nibs of the pen point.

Use the quill in regular ink or make up
your own ink from ripe pokeberries
and a little water. Or try some of
the colored juices from other plants,
or some of the darker dyes described
elsewhere in this book.

MUSICAL INSTRUMENTS

MORACHE

Not too musical, but often used by the western Indians for
accompaniment to other rhythm instruments, is a device
consisting of a smooth stick or dowel; a second stick in
which notches have been cut; and some form of resonator.
This is called a "morache".

MATERIALS NEEDED:

A dowel or round stick of hardwood about 1/2" by 12"

A hard or softwood stick about 3/4" by 18"

A large dried gourd, a #10 tin can, or other hollow device
to act as a resonator

HOW TO MAKE:

Cut a series of notches on one
    side of the larger stick,
    making them about 1/4"
    deep and 1/2" apart,
    starting at one end and
    extending about 2/3 of the
    length of the stick.

Trim the un-notched end to
    act as a handle.

HOW TO USE:

Place the notched end of the larger stick on the resonator
    which should be lying on the ground or table. Rub a-
    cross the notches with a rhythmic motion with the dowel
    held in one hand, and the handle of the notched stick
    held in the other.

The resonator amplifies the sound and improves the quality
    of the tone.

Practice until you can achieve a good rhythm.   Let someone
    accompany you on a tom-tom.

A GOURD DANCE RATTLE

Gourds, Horn, and Turtle Shells make effective dance rattles for use in Indian dances and ceremonies. Of these the
gourd rattles are, by far, the easiest to make.

MATERIALS NEEDED:

Gourds 3-5" in diameter and 5-7" long, well dried.

5/8"-3/4" dowel or broomstick for handles

1/2" drill

1/8" drill

Dried cherry pits or dried beans

Household cement

Water colors, airplane dope, or home-made Indian colors as described in another section of this book.

HOW TO MAKE:

Select gourds about 3" - 5" in diameter and from 5" - 7" in length. Dry them carefully until the shells are hard and the seeds rattle when the gourd is shaken.

Cut a handle from a dowel or piece of broomstick. The correct length should be the length of the gourd plus 7 inches.

With a 1/2" drill, drill holes in the opposite ends of the gourd.

Cut the dowel down to 1/2" diameter for all but 6 inches of its length. This 6 inch section will form the handle of the completed rattle. At the 6 inch point on the handle, cut a shoulder to fit against the end of the gourd.

Remove the seeds from the gourd through the holes drilled in the ends. It may be necessary to break some of them up with a stiff hooked wire in order to get them out through the holes.

In place of the seeds, put a dozen or so dried cherry pits or pea beans.

Insert the handle through both holes in the gourd and cement it into place at both ends.

Where the handle projects for about 1" through the end of the
gourd rattle, drill a 1/8" hole as close to the gourd as
possible, and cement a small wooden peg in this hole to
help in holding the handle in place.

Decorate the rattle with water colors, airplane dope, or with
your own Indian paints as described on page 64 of this
book.

A HORN DANCE RATTLE

MATERIALS NEEDED:

Medium sized cow horn

Handsaw

Scraps of soft wood about 3/4" in thickness

Small brads

1/16" drill

1/2" drill

5/8" - 3/4" dowel or broomstick for handle

Dried cherry pits, pea beans, or small pebbles

Sharp knife or broken glass for scraping horn

Fine sandpaper

Neutral shoe polish

Piece of yarn

Colored fluff feathers

Household cement

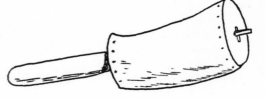

HOW TO MAKE:

Cut both ends from a cow's horn, making the cut surfaces
parallel to each other, and leaving 5" to 7" of horn for
the rattle.

Place the open ends of the rattle on pieces of soft wood about
3/4" in thickness and with a pencil trace around the inside of the horn. Cut these pieces of wood to shape on
the drawn lines and carefully fit them into the open ends
of the horn. Sandpaper or trim with a sharp knife to
make them fit snuggly. Fasten them in place with small
brads. It may be necessary to drill 1/16 inch holes in
the horn to accommodate the brads.

Drill 1/2" holes through the center of each piece of wood in
the ends of the rattle.

Make a handle as described above under "A Gourd Dance
Rattle".

Before inserting the handle, add a few dried cherry pits,
pea beans, or small pebbles, then insert the handle and
fasten by cementing, and the use of a small wooden peg
as described above for the Gourd Rattle.

Finish the horn by scraping, sandpapering, and polishing
with a neutral shoe polish.

To give an authentic Indian appearance, cement two or three
small colored fluff feathers to a cord or yarn, and attach to the tip of the rattle.

A TURTLE SHELL DANCE RATTLE

MATERIALS NEEDED:

Shell of either a Box Turtle or Snapping Turtle

1/2" drill

106

1/8" drill

5/8" - 3/4" dowel or broomstick for handle

Household cement

HOW TO MAKE:

The shells of the Box Turtle or Snapping Turtle are pre-
ferred to other varieties. The Box Turtle has a hinged
lower shell which will stay shut. Other kinds of turtle
shells will need to be laced. The Box Turtle is a land-
living turtle, while the Snapping Turtle is usually found
in the water.

When you have obtained a turtle shell, clean out the inside
as well as you are able, and then place the shell in a
container of water, boiling it for 1 to 3 hours, keeping
a careful watch to make sure
that the outer layer of the shell
does not start to peel off. One
hour will usually be enough depending upon the size and thickness of the shell. The shell
will soften, and the remaining
cleaning may now be done on
the inside of the shell.

When the shell has been cleaned,
force both the front and back
parts of the lower shell tightly
against the upper shell and
clamp them in place until the
shell cools, when they will stay
in place.

Drill 1/2" holes in the ends of the
shell; the first one in the flap
of the lower shell at the head
end, and the second in the upper
shell at the tail end, about 1/2"

from the end of the shell. These two holes should be centered and must line up as the place for the handle of the rattle to be inserted.

Cut a handle from a dowel or broomstick as described in the sections on horn and gourd rattles, insert and fasten with cement and a wooden peg as described. Add fluff feathers if desired.

Other types of turtle shells will need to be laced together with rawhide or leather thongs, and are much more difficult to make into rattles.

A CORN-STALK VIOLIN

Do you remember, as a small boy on the farm, making a squeaky violin from a section of cornstalk, using a smaller piece of cornstalk as a bow?

HOW TO MAKE:

Select a sizeable straight stalk of corn, cutting a section from the stalk on the outside of two of the joints or nodes of the stalk. This will leave a section of stalk about one foot long, with a joint or node at each end.

With a sharp knife, cut four slits lengthways from joint to joint, and about 1/8" apart. This will make three "strings". Carefully pry up these strings, and slide under them a tiny wooden bridge with three small notches about 1/4" apart on the top of the bridge. Slip the strings into these notches.

Use a small corn stalk for the bow.

You won't be able to play a tune, but can make some peculiar squeaky sounds.

A FLUTE FROM A PUMPKIN LEAF

Small boys once used pumpkin leaf stems for making a simple flute. Have you ever tried to make one?

HOW TO MAKE:

Select a pumpkin leaf with a straight stem, cutting it to about 12" in length.

Cut off the leaf at the solid part just beyond the hollow part of the stem.

With a knife, make a slit through the hollow part of the stem, about 1/2" from the point where the leaf has been cut off, making the slit through both sides of the stem.

Put this end of the stem in your mouth so that the slits are in the mouth, and blow. A deep sound should be produced.

Space three or four 1/4" holes, made with a knife, through the top of the stem, using these as finger holes to vary the tone of the flute.

If the first one doesn't work well, try another.

A VOICE DISGUISER

From a piece of hollow bamboo, 3 or 4 inches long, cut a 3/4" notch about 3/4" from each end, and on opposite sides the bamboo.

Place a piece of thin tissue or tracing paper over each end and tie tightly with strong thread. With a pin or small nail, make a hole in the edge of each tissue membrane, close to the bamboo at one edge of the hole.

To use, talk or sing into either of the notches. You will
notice that your voice is well disguised.

BONE CRAFTS

Bones are available for the asking (from the butcher), and
for the finding out in the woods and fields. They were the
Indian's sources of material for arrow points, awls, fish-
hooks, spear points, etc.

We can also use them in a nature crafts program to make
such things as neckerchief slides, napkin rings, finger rings,
trophies, etc.

An important part in using bone is the proper cleaning and
bleaching of the material.

A NECKERCHIEF SLIDE

MATERIALS NEEDED:

Marrow bone (leg bone of a cow, steer, or other large animal)

Household bleach

Sharp knife or broken glass

Medium file, either flat or triangular

Fine sandpaper

Sharp pointed awl

Handsaw

HOW TO MAKE:

Cut a 1 inch section of marrow bone.

Boil it for an hour or so, and then soak it in household bleach for a day or so.

Dry the bone well, and then scrape or file both the outside and inside to get the bone ring to the desired thickness and size.

Finish with fine sandpaper.

A design may be scratched, filed, or carved into the bone. Fine lines, scratched into the bone with a sharp pointed awl or knife, may have colored or India ink rubbed into them to make the design stand out.

Add a coat of shellac, spray plastic, clear lacquer, or nail polish to protect the design.

NAPKIN RINGS, FINGER RINGS, TROPHIES

These may be made by exactly the same process as the neckerchief ring described above, but will need different sized sections of bone. A napkin ring should have about a 1-1/2" diameter hollow center, and should be about 2" long. A finger ring would need an opening from 1/2 to 5/8" in diameter, with the section of bone cut to about 1/2" in length.

Trophies may be made from very large bones, carefully cleaned and bleached, and with the name of the Boy Scout Patrol, the Camp name, or other information scratched into the bone with a sharp pointed awl and the design colored with colored or India Inks.

Add a coat of shellac, spray plastic, or lacquer to protect the design.

CRAFTS WITH NUTS

Whole nuts, and even the empty shells have abundant uses in nature and crafts projects. Let's see what some of them are.

PECANS

Pecans with their smooth shells are used to make faces for dolls, lapel ornaments, pins, salt and pepper shakers.

Using scraps of cotton or woolen material, bits of felt, India ink, tempera colors or airplane dope, household cement, and scissors, you can design your own doll faces, hair, kerchiefs, clothes, etc.

A Lapel Ornament - Take a smooth pecan, and use India ink, airplane dope, or tempera colors for the eyes and mouth. Do not try to draw a nose. Cut pieces of black, yellow, or red felt for hair, cementing it at the top of the nut head, and reaching nearly to the bottom of the nut on the sides. Cut fringes in the ends of the felt hair. Cover the top of the head where the felt is cemented, with small coils or pompoms of yarn, tied with a fine thread, and then cemented or sewn in place.

Fasten a safety pin to the back of the head by sewing it to the felt hair, and the lapel ornament is completed.

A Second Lapel Ornament - Paint all of the features including the hair onto a pecan. Again, do not try to paint a nose for this is most difficult. Cut a 6" triangle from material having a tiny all-over pattern and cement it near the center of the back of the head.

Gather the material under the chin, up around the sides of the head, and tie tightly at the top of the head, cementing where necessary to hold the material in place.

Decorate this head-dress with tiny flowers at the ears or neckline, or at the top of the head. These may come from some old hat or other lapel ornament, and sewn on the tiny head-dress.

Sew a safety pin at the back, and the lapel ornament is completed.

A Cannibal Lapel Ornament - Obtain two small bone, metal,
or plastic rings about 3/4" in diameter. Tie these together with black thread or yarn, but far enough apart
so that the thread or yarn may be cemented to the top
of the pecan head, and the rings will hang at the sides
as though attached to the ears of a cannibal.

Wrap a strand of black yarn about 15 times around three
fingers and tie tightly at some point. Opposite the point
where this yarn is tied, cut through the loops of yarn.
This is the cannibal's hair, and should be cemented to
the top of the pecan head with the tie at the center of the
top of the head.

With scissors, trim the hair to bangs at the front, and
the rest of the hair in a jagged style.

Paint round or oval eyes on the face of the pecan. Add
a large mouth. To make the rings often worn around a
cannibal's neck, cut out tiny circles of felt, two or three
of each of two colors. The circles should be about 1/2"
in diameter. Cement alternate colored rings together,
and attach with cement at the bottom of the cannibal head.

Cement a small piece of felt to the back of the head and
sew a safety pin to the felt.

If a hanging cannibal head is desired, tie a piece of yarn
to the hair where it is tied at the top of the cannibal head.
Make a small loop of this yarn, and sew it to a small
circle of felt about 1-1/2" above the top of the head.
Sew a safety pin to the back of this piece of felt and the
pin is completed.

Salt and Pepper Shakers - Carefully cut the blunt ends from
two matching pecans. Scrape out the insides of the nuts
with a small sharp knife. Use a fine drill to make pour-
ing holes in the sharp ends of the pecans. Cut corks to
fit the bottoms.

Polish, lacquer, or shellac the nuts if desired.

WALNUTS

Walnuts, especially the empty shells, have many uses in crafts. They can be used in Christmas decorations, jewelry, tiny toys, in nature plaques, or in many other ways that you may discover for yourself.

Tree Ornaments - Paint walnut shells in gold, silver, or
   red using quick drying bright colored enamels or lac-
   quers. Airplane dope is an excellent lacquer, is readily
   available, and dries almost instantaneously. Cement a
   red or green string to one end of the shell for tying the
   decoration to the tree. Half shells, with the tying cord
   cemented between the halves of the shells, are even
   better than the whole nuts for they will not attract mice,
   squirrels, etc., in storage.

   Sequins may be cemented to the colored shells to add
   interest.

   For another ornament, use half shells, cut out flower
   shapes 2" - 3" in diameter from construction paper,
   and cement the half shells to the paper to make the flower centers. The shells may be cemented to the flowers
   either side up, and may be decorated with bright colors.
   String a cord through one of the petals for hanging.

   Still another ornament may be made using half shells,
   painting the outsides of the shells, and cementing a
   string to one end for hanging. Inside the half shell, cement tiny pieces of native materials to create a land-
   scape scene. Tiny pieces of ground pine, dried grass,
   and cotton may be used to make a winter scene. These
   scenes can make real conversation pieces on your
   Christmas Tree.

   A Christmas Bird is made by cutting the outline of a
   bird from colored construction paper, cementing half
   shells to each side of the paper to make the body of the
   bird, and then cementing construction paper wings to
   the shells.

Walnut Belts - Interesting belts are made from cross sections of black walnuts. Place the walnuts in a vise and
cut them crossways into 1/8" or 3/16" slices, using a
sharp hacksaw.

Cut a dozen or so of the nuts into slices before select-
ing the pieces for making a belt. Choose the slices that
are the nearest in size and shape, or select them in
graduated sizes, perhaps using first a large and then a
small one, or with the larger ones at the rear and the
smaller ones at the front of the belt. File and sandpaper the cut surfaces smooth and coat with colorless
nail polish. Lace the walnut slices on two heavy colored
cords, lacing each slice from the back to the front,
across the center section of the slice, and out through
the back again. The slices may be held in place by
tying the cords between each slice, or colored wooden
beads may be strung on each cord between the nut
slices.

Tie a loop in the cord at one end of the belt, to be slip-
ped over the last slice at the other end, to hold the belt
in place on the wearer.

Walnut Buttons - Slice the nuts as described above. File and
polish or lacquer the slices. The center section of the
nut slice forms the shank of the button for sewing to material. Loops are better than buttonholes for use with
walnut buttons, or the buttons may be used for ornamen-
tation only.

Walnut Tie Slide - Using one of the buttons as made above,
remove the section at the center of the walnut slice.
File smooth and polish, lacquer and it will make a fine
tie slide.

ALMONDS

With a tiny drill or sharp awl, make holes through a number
of almonds at the sides of the shells near the broad end.

These are for stringing the almonds to make a necklace or
bracelet.

Paint the almonds with lacquer, airplane dope, or enamel,
or if you prefer a natural color, shellac the nuts. Allow ample time to dry. While they are drying, cut out
tiny felt leaves from scraps of green felt or glove leather. The leaves should be slightly smaller than the almonds. String the almonds and the leaves alternately,
using a needle and heavy thread. The resulting necklace will prove very attractive.

Make a bracelet in the same manner, but use elastic thread
for stringing, and tying the thread when the bracelet is
large enough to slip over the wrist with the elastic
stretched.

Another method of making a necklace, is to make two of the
tiny leaves for each almond. Using a very fine wire,
thread the wire through a leaf, an almond, then another
leaf. Bring the wires together at the top of the almond,
twisting them once or twice, then forming a tiny loop
and twisting again. Several almonds are fixed in this
manner. In stringing, the string is run through the
loops, rather than through the leaves and almonds as
in the necklace described above.

These almonds and leaves may be combined with other nuts
in making costume jewelry such as lapel ornaments.

HAZEL NUTS

Hazel nuts make excellent buttons, flowers, etc.

To Make Buttons - Use tiny screw eyes, screwed into the
base of the nut. These tiny screw eyes may be obtained
from most craft supply houses. You may find it necessary to start the screw eyes with a tiny nail or pin hole,
or a small awl.

Color the buttons with enamel or lacquer if desired.

To Make Flowers - cut little flower shapes from pieces of
colored felt, 1/2" to 3/4" in diameter. Place the screw
eye through the center of the felt flower and then screw
into the hazel nut. Decorate them with tiny spots or
lines of colored enamel or lacquer to make the flower
centers. Use clusters of these hazel nut flowers, sewn
to a piece of felt for a lapel pin. Sew a safety pin to the
back of the felt for attaching the lapel to the clothing.

Combine some of these hazel nut flowers, with the almonds and leaves described above as a lapel ornament
on a piece of felt. Add one or two hemlock cones, using
a fine wire twisted around the base of the cone, and
forming a tiny loop similar to those on the almonds.

Use the hazel nut flowers with the almonds and leaves to
make a bracelet by running a double cord through the
screw eyes and wire loops, tying each nut in place as
they are threaded, and about 1/2" apart. Make a small
loop in the cord at the end of the bracelet, just large
enough to slip over the last nut. This will fasten the
bracelet in place on the wrist.

OTHER NUT BUTTONS

Small nuts, acorns, pits, etc. of many kinds may be made
into interesting buttons by removing the insides; filling them
with plastic wood, and inserting a tiny screw eye. Allow to
dry thoroughly before using.

They may be polished, colored, covered with a clear lacquer,
or left natural.

In addition to their uses as buttons, try stringing them for a
necklace or bracelet to match the buttons.

PEACH PITS

Peach Pit Tie Slides - These are similar to the walnut tie
slides. Cut a slice from each side of a peach pit,

scrape or file smooth; polish or lacquer, and the slide
is completed.

Peach Pit Buttons - Follow directions for making walnut
buttons.

SHELL CRAFTS

Some illustrations of shells being used in making "Nature
Plaques" were shown in the book, "Creative Nature Crafts"
by R. O. Bale.

GENERAL DIRECTIONS:

Shells of many kinds may be picked up along the ocean
beaches. Snail shells are found in most lakes, ponds,
and streams, and some varieties may be found in the
woods and fields.

Most of the shells used in craft projects, however, are purchased from craft supply houses.

Native shells may be cleaned by soaking in a household
bleach, then washed and dried.

EQUIPMENT NEEDED:

Jewelry findings such as pin backs, earring backs, plastic
discs, jump rings, chain, clasps, etc.

Razor blade

Household Cement

Tweezers

Sharp Pointed Awl

Punching Board (soft wood)

PUNCHING HOLES IN SHELLS:

Hold the shell on a punching board, and punch holes where
desired, using a sharp pointed awl with a twisting motion and not too much pressure.

A SHELL BRACELET

Select small but interesting shells of different kinds.

Punch a small hole at the end of each shell.

Paint shells with a clear lacquer or nail polish.

Add jump rings, and attach to a small chain, like a charm
bracelet. Add a clasp for fastening the bracelet.

SHELL EAR RINGS

Cement four flat shells to a small plastic disc. Lucine
shells are best for this. At the center of each of the
flat shells, cement a small cup shell. When dry cement
to earring backs.

Experiment with other shell earrings using a variety of shell
types and colors. If the earring is not a balanced design, remember that the earring for the opposite side
must face in the other direction, and the design attached
accordingly.

SHELL PLAQUES

Both natural and cut shells may be used in creating beautiful
plaques either for use at home or for sale. They may be attached to a background of wood, cardboard, plastic, or other
material. Shells are attached with household cement, being
careful not to use too much for extra cement is unsightly
and may spoil the appearance of the plaque.

SEED CRAFTS

Seeds have many decorative uses. When dried they can be cemented to boxes, paper plates, plaques, shingles, glass, plastic, etc. in many decorative patterns. They may be strung as beads for necklaces and bracelets, or even made into hot-pads. Some of the most useful seeds for craft work are listed below. Some are large enough to string while others are so tiny that they may need to be cemented in quantity as a background for designs of other seeds.

Apricots	Pepper
Beans	Poppy
Buckwheat	Radishes
Cabbage	Rye
Corn	Tomato
Dates	Watermelon
Muskmelon	Wheat
Peach	

CORN FLOWERS

Kernels of field corn may be very decorative.

Use them for a frame around a mounted poem, glueing or cementing them as a border around the verses, and mounting the finished product on heavy cardboard or plywood.

Used with small acorns or acorn cups, or with sections of pine or hemlock cones, they make effective flowers containing the best fall colors, for the corn will show yellow with tips of brown, rust, and red, and the cones a beautiful brown.

Use corn in nature jewelry, too, for pins, brooches, and
earrings.

LEAF PICTURES

Grandmother used to gather colored leaves in the fall, using
them to brighten the house during the long winters when
flowers were not available.

Gather your leaves at the height of their fall color and press
them for three or four days. Pressing is best done between pieces of absorbent paper towels or blotting paper
under pressure.

When pressed, cement the leaves on cardboard backings, to
produce outdoor scenes. Use the leaves as they are,
or reshape them with a pair of scissors to represent
trees, mountains, streams, houses, etc.

Use colored paper for streams, lakes, ponds, etc., if desired.

Mount scene under glass or plastic.

MULLEIN ROSETTES

Collect the leaves of mullein in the fall and let them dry to
a soft beautiful velvety green. (Mullein is distinguished
during the summer by its tall, thick stems. During the
fall and winter, the leaves are found in the form of a
rosette growing close to the ground.)

Cover heavy cardboard with black velvet, and stitch the mullein leaves to this background, using the leaves as a
frame. Add dried seed pods, nuts, acorns, and grasses
to give a three dimensional effect to the picture.

MILKWEED FLUFF BALLS

A few people still know how to gather and fashion the fluffy
silken milkweed balls as my grandmother did when I was
small. They were used to throw over picture frames; over
the corner of the mantle; or as a part of a curtain tie-back;
or for any other place that was in need of a soft bit of decoration.

They were usually hung at the ends of different lengths of
ribbon and sometimes were dyed in pastel shades. Enclosed
in the finest of net or chiffon, they were called "silk illu-
sions". Ladies sometimes filled pillows with the fluff, adding a sachet for a fine scent. Sometimes they were used for
trimming hats.

HOW TO MAKE:

Pick the milkweek pods just before they burst, but while the
     fluff is still moist. Remove the outside green shell of
     the milkweed pod, and dip the remaining cone of the
     milkweed floss in water. Carefully remove the seeds.

Pick apart the separate tufts of the floss and lay them across
     a piece of string at the center of the tufts. When you
     have enough tufts to make a medium sized ball, tie the
     string tightly around the center of the tufts. If you wish
     to dye the floss, do so at this point, using any household
     dye.

Hang the milkweed fluff balls in the sunshine to dry.

When dry, tie several of the fluff balls to lengths of baby
     ribbon and use for decorations.

(Try the same procedure with the fluff from thistles.)

POMANDER BALLS

Pomander balls were once used to give a delightful fragrance
to clothing, handkerchiefs, etc.

To make a pomander ball, select a thin skinned lemon, orange, or lime. With a darning needle or sharp pointed pick, pierce the skin and insert cloves either in an all-over pattern, or in some simple geometric design.

Roll lemons and limes in nutmeg, and oranges in cinnamon, with as thick a coating as possible. Wrap them in foil and store for several weeks.

Tie a loop of ribbon to the foil for hanging, and use the pomander ball with its foil wrapping, in your clothes closet or dresser drawer.

At one time pomander balls were carried about by people, supposedly as a safeguard against infection.

BALL OF CLOVES

This could be called a pomander ball, too, for the name comes from the French word "pomme" for apple, and an apple is the base of this ball.

Select a good apple and stick cloves through the skin, pushing them in so that only the head of the cloves can be seen. Cover the entire surface of the apple in this way. Then tie a ribbon around the center of the apple, making a loop for hanging in the clothes closet where it will impart a delightful fragrance. (An ice pick or awl may help in making the holes for the cloves to be pushed into the apple.)

SACHETS

Flowers and herbs make sweet smelling sachets.

Pick herbs, sweet clover, rose petals, mint, etc., at the peak of bloom. Dry them thoroughly. When dry, crush them to perfume clothing, handkerchiefs, etc.

Many flowers have a lovely fragrance even after they have
    been dried. When they have been gathered and dried,
    break off the petals and place them in jars, using
    separate jars for each kind of flower. Keep the jars
    covered until you are ready to use the petals. Then
    make little bags of silk or other material, fill them
    with the dried petals, and tie them with ribbons.

Use these sachets for gifts, or to place in a drawer with
    your own linens.

Roses, sweet-peas, geraniums, and other flowers with a
    substantial fragrance when they are alive, will make
    the best sachets after they have dried.

Perhaps you would like a mixture of two or more varieties
    of flower petals in your sachet. Experiment with them
    to get the perfume that you like best.

MAGNOLIA LEAF SKELETONS (ANGEL FEATHERS)

Skeletonized magnolia leaves, sometimes called "Angel
Feathers", are fragile, light, and beautiful, and once you
have seen them, you will understand whence came the name
"Angel Feathers".

They may be used on gift packages, in winter dried flower
and leaf arrangements, in corsages, or mounted under glass
or plastic.

MATERIALS NEEDED:

Fresh Magnolia leaves

Household bleach in a detergent

Sugar

Water

Aluminum or enamel pan (3-4quart size)

124

Absorbent paper such as paper towels or blotters

Dull knife

HOW TO MAKE:

Add 2/3 cup of detergent containing a bleaching agent to 6
cups of water and bring to a boil.

Place 10-12 fresh magnolia leaves in this solution and boil
for 15-20 minutes, keeping the leaves well covered.
Allow to cool in the solution.

Remove the leaf on a flat surface, and with a dull knife,
carefully scrape the fleshy material from both sides of
the leaf. If a strong water spray is available, use this
to wash the green chlorophyl material from both sides
of the leaf. A soft fine brush may help in removing
the last of the green material from the leaf.

When the color has all been removed from the leaves, place
them under pressure between layers of absorbent paper.
If green color still shows in the skeleton, mix two
tablespoons household bleach per quart of water and
immerse the leaves in this solution until they are bleached white. This should take about one hour.

Allow the leaves to dry for a few days under pressure.

To color the leaves, dip in a household dye before drying
and pressing; or spray with metallic colors or enamels
after they have been pressed and dried.

Use florist's wire and tape for stems if the leaves are to be
used in arrangements with other materials, or in corsages.

BAYBERRY CANDLES

If you are fortunate enough to live along the coast, you should
be able to obtain enough bayberries to make your own candles.

Bayberry plants have a curious greyish berry about 1/8" in diameter, coated with tiny nodules of wax. The wax may be extracted and used in making candles which do not drip, and which give off a highly agreeable odor. In fact, the wax is so desirable that small portions of it are often mixed with other kinds of wax for candle making.

Use the bayberry candles for gifts, as well as for your own enjoyment.

OBTAINING THE WAX:

Since only a small portion of the berry is wax, a considerable amount of the berries must be gathered to obtain enough wax for candles.

After gathering two or more quarts of the berries, place them in hot water and gradually bring it to a boil. The wax will melt and rise to the top. Skim the wax from the surface, gradually removing all foreign materials from the wax.

When it has been partially cleaned, straining through a fine strainer will remove most of the remaining foreign materials. The wax may have to go through several meltings in boiling water to be completely cleaned.

MAKING THE CANDLES:

Melt the wax in the top of a double boiler, or in a tin can used as a double boiler. Keep the water in the bottom of the double boiler hot enough to keep the wax in a melted state while the candles are being made.

Obtain some candle-wicking if possible. Many stores have candle-wicking such as is used in making candle-wick bed spreads; or if candle-wicking is unobtainable, use a heavy but soft cotton cord for the wick. Cut this in pieces a little longer than the length desired for the finished candles. Tie a loop in one end of the wick for hanging.

Dip the wicks in the melted wax, keeping the wicks as
straight as possible, and allowing the wax to harden
between dips. Hang the candle on a nail by its loop of
wicking while the wax is hardening. This will take but
a few minutes.

Continue dipping until the desired size of candle has been
reached.

If old candle molds are available, wash them well and then
use them for casting candles. The wicks are placed in
the molds before the wax is poured, tying one end of
the wicking outside the small end of the mold, and the
other end to a stick to hold the wicking in the center of
each of the molds.

When the wicks are in place, pour the melted wax into the
molds and allow it to harden.

Candles are removed from the molds after the wax has
hardened, by dipping the molds into hot water until the
candles loosen and can be removed.

SAVE THE PIECES:

Since bayberry wax is not too easily obtained, save all scraps
and candle ends for reuse in making new candles. If there
is not enough bayberry wax available for several candles,
mix what is available with the melted ends of other candles.
You will still get some of the color and fragrance of the real
bayberry candles.

FLOWER PETAL BEADS

Beads made from the petals of flowers have a charming fragrance of their own and will bring back nostalgic memories
to many older persons who may have made them in their own
childhood.

The petals, preferably roses, are chopped very fine, placed in a metal container and left there for one week. Keep them from drying out by occasionally sprinkling lightly with water.

At the end of one week, mix into a soft doughy mass with more water added if needed.

Form beads by rolling between the thumb and finger and pushing the bead over a needle or wire to make the hole in the bead. Allow several days for hardening.

Before putting the beads away to harden, the beads may be pressed into desired shapes such as a rosebud shape, using a toothpick as a modeling tool.

You might also try adding a little flour and stirring the mixture well, before rolling the beads into shape.

CRYSTALLIZING SOLUTION FOR CARDS

This is an idea for making sparkling Christmas and other cards, using a crystallized salt solution for decorating. It may be used on colored papers, seals, tags, etc.

MATERIALS NEEDED:

Epsom salts

Water

Small paint brush

Cards, tags, or colored paper to decorate

HOW TO MAKE:

Bring 1/2 cup of water to a boil. Stir in a little more epsom salts than will completely dissolve. This will make a saturated solution.

HOW TO USE:

Use the solution while it is warm. With a paint brush,
   paint the solution over the part of the picture to have a
   crystalline decoration, or use it on portions of cards,
   tags, etc. As the solution dries, it will form into
   crystals having the appearance of snowflakes. The
   crystals will not stick too well on glossy papers, so it
   is found most effective when used on papers with a soft
   finish. Try using colored construction papers, decorating them with crystals, and then cutting out the decorated parts and pasting them on paper of another color
   to complete the cards or tags.

Try cutting out letters, decorating them with crystals and
   using them on a background of another color.

SNOWSTORM IN A GLASS JAR

Our great-grandparents often had a miniature snowstorm
inside a small glass container, as a curiosity on the table in
the front parlor. I was fascinated by one that my grandmother had.

TO MAKE ONE:

Select a round glass jar of any size, but preferably a small
   one of an attractive shape.

Using household cement, fasten a small china or plastic
   figure, and a few bare twigs to the inside of the cover
   where they will be in the snow storm.

Fill the jar almost full of water to which a very tiny amount
   of blue food coloring has been added.

In the water, place a small amount of moth flakes, the a-
   mount depending upon the size of the jar used.
   Christmas snow (mica) may be used in place of the moth
   flakes if it is more easily obtained.

Apply plenty of cement to the rim of the jar cover, and screw into place, adding more cement around the outside of the jar cover where it meets the jar. This must be a waterproof joint when the cement is dry, for the jar is to be inverted.

Let the jar stand for several days for the cement to dry thoroughly, then invert it to stand on the jar cover.

A slight shake will send the "snow" swirling throughout the jar, creating a miniature snowstorm.

PLASTER OF PARIS BOOK—ENDS

A set of book-ends made of Plaster of Paris makes a fine background for mounting favorite nature specimens, small animal skulls, shells, cones, rock, and mineral samples.

MATERIALS NEEDED:

Plaster of Paris

Scrap lumber

Aluminum Foil

Plastic Dish

Spoon or stick for mixing plaster

Nature specimens for mounting

HOW TO MAKE:

Cut two pieces of scrap lumber about 5" square. Nail these together at right angles to make a form for the book-end.

Cover the wooden form with aluminum foil to prevent plaster sticking to the wood, and to make the plaster easier to remove when it has hardened.

In a plastic dish, mix plaster and water to a thick creamy consistency.

Watch the plaster carefully for it is to be used just as it starts to harden.

Just as it begins to harden, place spoonfuls of the plaster on the aluminum foil form, covering the base and building the plaster up at the back of the form, making the center at least one inch thick and tapering off towards the edges of the form. Work fast before the plaster hardens.

If the plaster hardens too fast and does not spoon easily, discard the remaining plaster and mix up a fresh batch to build up the book-ends. You need to work very fast for the plaster remains in a useable condition for only a very few minutes.

As soon as the book-end has been built up enough to satisfy you, press your nature specimens into the plaster where they will remain permanently. If possible plan the arrangement of the specimens ahead of time, for it will be difficult to make any changes once they have been pressed into the plaster.

Allow the plaster to harden, then remove the wooden form and peel off the aluminum foil. Let the plaster dry thoroughly for several days, then glue or cement a piece of felt to the bottoms of the book-ends to protect furniture.

USING EGG SHELLS

Broken egg shells make a delightful crackle finish when applied to boxes, old compacts, picture frames, etc. This is a glamorizing treatment.

A CRACKLE FINISH

Break the egg shell into very small pieces. Spread glue on the surface to be "crackled", then press the broken shells into the glue. Let the glue dry, then paint, varnish, or shellac.

EGG DECORATING

Egg decorating goes back to the days of the pagans when eggs were the symbol of springtime and gaily decorated eggs were used in holiday and religious celebrations. The custom of decorating eggs for Easter probably comes down from those ancient ceremonies.

How to Prepare Eggs

Pierce the ends of uncooked eggs with a needle or other sharp instrument. Blow through the hole in one end of the egg catching the contents in a glass or bowl for cooking uses. If the contents do not blow readily, make the holes a little larger, but keep them just as small as possible.

The blown shells have many uses.

Make an Egg Basket -

Use an awl to chip small pieces of shell from one side of the egg, making an opening for tiny plants, flowers, leaves, ferns, or moss. Chip a 1" to 2" hole, leaving the blowing holes intact. Thread a ribbon through these holes, making a loop for hanging the basket.

Make an Egg Garden -

Cut off the smaller end of a blown egg with sharp pointed
   scissors, or chip it away carefully with an awl.   Fill
   the egg shell with soil or vermiculite and plant garden
   seeds.   Set the egg shells upright in muffin tins, holding them upright with soil, sand, or vermiculite.   Add
   water to the tins, and it will soak through the egg shells
   to start the seeds growing.

Make Easter Faces -

Paint features such as eyes, nose, mouth, and hair on one
   side of a blown egg.   Or glue or cement crepe paper,
   yarn, raffia, or wool hair and mustaches to the egg
   head.

Make hats of bits of scrap material or paper, and decorate
   with bits of ribbon, feathers, beads, etc.

Make an egg stand from a piece of heavy paper cemented
   into a cone shape, and with the point of the cone cut off.
   To this stand cement paper bows, neckties, ruffles, or
   collars, and place the egg head on the stand.

Make Animals -

To make a duck or baby chicken, cut a small diamond
   shaped piece of yellow or orange construction paper.
   Fold double and cement into place at one end of the
   blown egg.   Paint eyes in the proper place and place
   the egg on a paper egg stand made as described above.

To make a rabbit, cut ears from pink construction paper.
   Slit for 1/4" at the bottom.   Bend one side of the slit
   in, and one side out and cement in place on the large
   end of the blown egg, facing outward.   Paint features
   on the egg and cement broom straws on the egg for
   whiskers.   Place on a paper egg stand and add a bow
   tie made of paper.

VEGETABLE BLOCK PRINTING

Potatoes, carrots, turnips, or any other vegetable that will
have a smooth surface when sliced, can be used for making
block prints. In the same way we can also make block
prints from soap erasers, dowels, spools, etc.

HOW TO MAKE:

Cut the vegetable into two pieces with a single slice, leaving
a perfectly smooth surface. Let these pieces dry for
several hours until they begin the dry or "cork over".

As soon as the vegetables are dry enough to work, draw simple designs using broad lines and large masses on the
flat surface of the cut vegetable. If necessary, use
carbon paper, and trace the design selected. Such simple shapes as stars, Christmas Trees, etc., are
easiest to do.

With a sharp knife, cut away the unwanted part of the surface
around the design, leaving the design standing out 1/8"
to 1/4" from the surrounding area.

HOW TO USE:

To print, use block printing inks or artists oil colors. With
a rubber roller or brayer, roll out a small amount of
ink or paint on a piece of glass or on a sheet of waxed
paper laying on a flat surface.

Press the block print design into the rolled out ink or paint
and immediately press it onto the material to be printed.
Try this out several times on scrap material before
making the final prints, making certain that the design
is just as you want it. It may need a bit more trimming,
the paint or ink may be too thick or too thin, or you may
not be using the right amount of pressure.

If the printed design appears fuzzy around the edges, it
means that the ink or paint is too thin; and if it appears

smudged, the ink or paint is too thick. Most of the
printing inks and paints may be thinned with turpentine.

Use your completed vegetable block print to make borders
on such things as napkins, table cloths, gift wrapping
paper, dresser scarves, or use as a single print in one
corner of a sheet of stationery.

NOTES - When block printing, as the ink or paint dries on
the glass or waxed paper, add one or two drops of
turpentine or kerosene and mix well with a knife,
brush, or artists' spatula.

If tempera colors are more easily available than
block printing ink or artists' oil colors, use them
to paint the surface of the block print design, and
immediately pressing the design onto the material
to be printed. The tempera colors dry very quickly
and so must be applied directly to the block print
with a brush.

CRAYON BATIK

Crayon batik is not a nature craft, but is effective for de-
signing when tempera colors are available. They are used
for doing an all-over paint and crayon decoration.

HOW TO MAKE:

Using white paper, draw the desired designs with a light
colored crayon. Then brush the entire surface with a
thin dark colored tempera paint. The paint will not
stick to the crayon marks, but will color only the background.

TWO—COLOR CARNATIONS

Two color carnations are easily made.

Using a white carnation, cut off the end of the stem under water to prevent air bubbles forming in the tubes inside the stem.

Remove from the water and carefully split the stem for about six inches.

Place the split ends in separate glasses of water colored with ink or food coloring. Keep the carnation in bright light for a few hours. Watch the gradual change in color of the carnation petals as the colored water is drawn up into them.

LEAF SILHOUETTES

Hold a leaf against a sheet of white paper. Using a small sponge, rub the sponge over an ink pad, and then from the edges of the leaf, outwards onto the paper, leaving the silhouettes of the leaf on the paper.

Label each leaf print with the variety of leaf used.

FOIL PRINTS OF LEAVES

Place the dull side of heavy aluminum foil over the veined side of a leaf, and rub with the finger tips to produce detailed prints. These may be cut out and mounted on cardboard, or they may be colored with water colors or poster paints. The paints will not stick well to the aluminum, but will give an interesting splotched coloration to the foil leaves.

SHADOW PRINTS OF LEAVES

Place leaf between window and sheet of paper. Trace around the outline of the leaf; cut out the design drawn, and mount on construction paper. Label correctly.

WAXING AUTUMN LEAVES

We may preserve the beautiful colors found in autumn leaves by waxing them. We need an electric iron and a cake of paraffin. Using a moderately hot iron, rub the iron over a cake of paraffin, and then carefully iron both sides of the leaf. Experiment a little to get the correct temperature for the iron. If it is too hot, it will damage the leaf.

PRESERVING LEAVES WITH GLYCERINE

Leaves such as those of oak, beech, holly, ivy, and similar tough fibered leaves are among the best to preserve in glycerine.

MATERIALS NEEDED:

Glycerine

Water

Small jar

HOW TO MAKE:

Leaves to be preserved should be gathered early in the morning.

Crush the lower two inches of the stems with a hammer to split the fibers and enable them to absorb moisture more readily.

Place the stems in a jar containing two parts of water and one part of glycerine. The solution should cover the entire stem of each leaf.

It may take from three days to two weeks for the leaves to absorb the glycerine and get a beautiful glossy effect.

HOW TO USE:

Most leaves preserved in glycerine will last for years and
can be used in flower arrangements. Save left over
glycerine solution and use it again.

NOTE - Completely submerging some leaves such as ivy
and lily-of-the-valley, in a solution of equal parts
of water and glycerine, also works well. Leave
for about one week, then wipe and dry the leaves
carefully before placing in arrangements, or store
until needed.

CRAFT RECIPES

HIGH POLISH FOR WOODEN ARTICLES

Sandpaper the objects using a very fine sandpaper. Soak
them for about 12 hours in linseed oil, or apply plenty
of linseed oil with a paint brush and then let stand for
12 hours or more.

Wipe dry and rub well with a flannel rag.

Prepare a polish by mixing turpentine with melted beeswax
until it makes a thick paste.

Apply a very small amount of this paste to the wooden article, and polish with a soft cloth to a very high luster.

MODELING DOUGH

Mix together a full cup of flour, a scant cup of salt, and
about 1/4 cup of water. Add food coloring if desired.
Use the dough for modeling. It will harden slowly, but
when dry may be painted.

FINGER PAINTS

Place a heaping tablespoon of cornstarch in 1/4 cup of water and stir until well blended. Add one pint of water,
one tablespoon of soapflakes, bring to a boil and then
allow to cool.

To color, add food coloring or dry colors in small amounts
and stir well.

Finger paints are most effective on shiny paper such as
shelf paper. After using, allow the paper to dry, then
press on the back with a warm iron to smooth.

PAPIER-MACHE

Tear or cut newspapers into narrow strips. Dip each strip,
as it is used, into a mixture of flour and water, or thin
boilded cornstarch paste.

Apply the strips over molds such as dishes, fruit, balloons,
etc. applying several thicknesses with the strips running in all directions.

Allow the finished product to dry, then remove the mold and
paint or shellac the papier-mache form. If used over a
bowl or fruit not easy to remove, slice the papier-mache
form in half with a safety razor blade, remove the mold
and add a few more strips of the pasted paper over the
cut area.

To make removal of the mold easier, the first layer of
paper strips applied to the mold, should be dipped in
clear water instead of paste.

SELECTED BIBLIOGRAPHY

The following list of books, to the best knowledge of the author, provides the most useful references available for the type of material included in this book.

"Creative Nature Crafts" by Robert O. Bale, Burgess Publishing Co., 426 So. Sixth St., Minneapolis 15, Minn. 1959 $2.50

"Keeping Idle Hands Busy" by Marion R. Spear, Burgess Publishing Co., 426 So. Sixth St., Minneapolis 15, Minn.

"Native and Creative" by Thelma Stinson, Camping Services, Board of Education of the Methodist Church, P.O. Box 871, Nashville 2, Tenn. 1957 $.40

"Discover the Stars" by Gaylord Johnson and Irving Adler; Sentinel Books Publishers, Inc., 112 East 19th. St., New York 3, N.Y. 1954

"Primer for Star Gazers" by Harry M. Neeley, Harper's, New York $5.00

"Monthly Evening Sky Map" (quarterly) Celestial Map Publishing Co., P.O. Box 3, Pike Co., Shela, Penna. $.60 each

"Cub Scout Fun Book" Boy Scouts of America, New Brunswick, New Jersey 1956 $1.00

"Creative Crafts for Campers" by Catherine T. Hammett and Carol M. Horrocks; Association Press, 291 Broadway, New York 7, New York 1957 $6.95

"Nature Activities for Summer Camps" National Audubon Society, 1000 Fifth St., New York City, N.Y. 1950

"Nature Crafts for Camp and Playground" National Recrea-
tion Ass'n., 8 West 8th. St., New York 11, N.Y.

"Campcraft ABC's" by Catherine T. Hammett, Girl Scouts
of the U.S.A., 155 East 44th. St., New York 17, N.Y.

"How to Build a Nature Museum" by Vinson Brown, Little
Brown and Co., Boston, Mass. 1955 $2.50

"Field Book of Nature Activities" by William Hillcourt, G.
P. Putnam's Sons, 210 Madison Ave., New York 16,
N.Y. 1950 $3.95

"Book of Nature Hobbies" by Ted Pettitt, Didier Publishers,
660 Madison Ave., New York, N.Y. 1947 $3.50

"Use of Native Craft Materials" by Margaret E. Shanklin,
The Manual Arts Press, Peoria, Illinois 1947

"Exploring the Hand Arts" Girl Scouts of the U.S.A., 155
East 44th. St., New York 17, N.Y. 1955 $.65

"A Project in Arts and Crafts" by Harold M. Watts, Rural
Research Institute Inc., 500 Fifth Ave., New York 36,
N.Y. Free

"Handbook of Crafts" by Members of the League of New
Hampshire Arts and Crafts, Fawcett Book 152, Fawcett
Publications, Inc., Greenwich, Conn. 1952 $.75

"The Nature Book" (for boys and girls 8-12), by Helen Jill
Fletcher, Paxton-Slade Publishing Corp., New York,
N.Y. 1954

"Whittling Book" by Ben Hunt, Bruce Publishing Co., 400
N. Broadway, Milwaukee 1, Wisconsin 1944 $3.50

"Whittling and Woodcarving" by E. J. Tangerman, Whit-
tlesey House, McGraw-Hill Book Co., 330 West 42nd.
St., New York 36, N.Y.

"Things to Do With a Pocket Knife" by E. J. Tangerman, Remington Arms Co., Cutler Division, Bridgeport, Conn., 1934 Free

"How to Do Wood Carving" by John L. Lacey, Fawcett Book 248, Fawcett Publications, Inc., Greenwich, Conn. $.75

"Woodcraft" by Bernard S. Mason, A. S. Barnes and Co., 232 Madison Ave., New York 16, N.Y. 1939 $2.75

"Nature Crafts" by Ellsworth Jaeger, The Macmillan Co., 60 Fifth Ave., New York 11, N.Y. 1950 $2.50

"The Book of Arts and Crafts" by Marguerite Ickis and Reba S. Ash, Association Press, 291 Broadway, New York 7, N.Y. 1954 $9.95

"Folk Arts and Crafts" by Marguerite Ickis, Association Press, 291 Broadway, New York 7, N.Y. 1958 $5.95

"Creative Handicrafts" by M. R. Hutchins, Sentinel Books, 112 East 19th. St., New York 3, N.Y. 1938

Arts and Crafts With Inexpensive Materials" Girl Scouts of the U.S.A., 155 East 44th. St., New York 17, N.Y. 1947 $.50

"Pack-O-Fun" (The only scrap craft magazine) 741 Devon Ave., Park Ridge, Illinois $2.00 per year (10 issues)

Date Due

MAY 28 '63			
MAY 31 '65			
JUL 2 2 '65			
AUG 5 '66			
8-10-67			
MAY 3 1 1968			
JUN 1 1 1968			
JUL 2 1976			
FEB 0 8 1988			
WITHDRAWN			
	PRINTED	IN U. S. A.	